Hamlyn all-colour paperbacks

A. G. Forsdyke BSc PhD ARCS

The Weather Guide

illustrated by Angus McBride

Hamlyn · **London**
Sun Books · Melbourne

FOREWORD

Why didst thou promise such a beauteous day,
And make me travel forth without my cloak,
To let base clouds o'ertake me in my way . . . ?
W. Shakespeare, Sonnet 34.

From biblical times to the present day weather forecasting has attracted considerable interest. Its exponents have included the charlatan and soothsayer, taking advantage of widespread ignorance and susperstition; shrewd observers of wind and sky like farmers and sailors; and the modern scientific meteorologist. This book has no more to say of the first group; it is concerned with weather study as a science, but it recognizes the wisdom, expressed in weather lore, of those whose livelihood is earned out-of-doors.

Today weather study (meteorology) is a specialized science, involving physics and mathematics. This book attempts to present the subject to the ordinary reader; it asks of him no more than the most elementary physics, and no mathematics at all. The explanation of weather phenomena are over-simplified, but it is better to present the basic ideas in an easily understandable way than to confuse the reader with complexities – the latter are for the expert.

The arrangement of the book is, briefly, observing the weather, causes of weather, weather forecasting, climate, and applications of weather study in everyday life.

The author has drawn upon his experience of nearly 40 years with the Meteorological Office, U.K. Ministry of Defence. He gratefully acknowledges the help afforded by the publications listed at the end of the book, and especially by the National Meteorological Library at Bracknell, Berkshire.

A.F.

Published by The Hamlyn Publishing Group Limited
London · New York · Sydney · Toronto
Hamlyn House, Feltham, Middlesex, England
In association with Sun Books Pty Ltd Melbourne

SBN 600000990
Phototypeset by Jolly & Barber Limited, Rugby, England
Colour separations by Schwitter Limited, Zurich
Printed in England by Sir Joseph Causton & Sons Limited

CONTENTS

INTRODUCTION

The earth is enveloped by a vast ocean of air, called the **atmosphere**, at the bottom of which lives man. The total depth is about 100 miles, but at great heights the air is very thin, so that half the weight of the atmosphere is contained in the lowest $3\frac{1}{2}$ miles. This lower part is in a state of constant turmoil, the varied effects of which are recognized as weather.

Weather is something one has to live with, and, in the British Isles at least, it is a universal topic of conversation. In everyday language weather means such qualities as wet or fine, warm or cold, and until perhaps a hundred years ago these descriptive terms were adequate for most purposes. Since the growth of industry, however, the weather factor has become more significant economically and weather study has been put on an organized and scientific footing. Instead of descriptive terms, standardized terms are used. These apply chiefly to those factors, which are measured by instruments and specified numerically, like temperature and rainfall, but less precisely to some other factors like cloudiness and fog. The branch of science concerned with weather study is called **meteorology**.

Most countries maintain official meteorological services. As

Instrument enclosure of a meteorological station

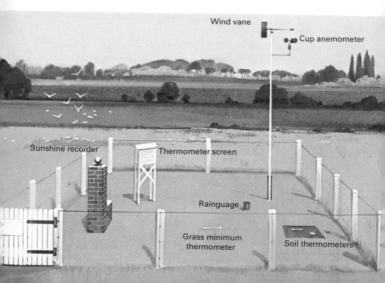

Weather ships report daily from fixed points far out to sea.

part of their functions these services have set up networks of **weather observing stations** at which regular observations are made and recorded according to internationally agreed procedures, at fixed hours of each day. This ensures that the weather at any station can be truly compared with that at any other.

Weather stations are of various kinds. Many provide the observations used in weather forecasting, while others are concerned only with a general picture of the day's weather. All reports are scrutinized and the stations inspected and the instruments checked by the controlling meteorological service.

Weather reports from the vast ocean areas are supplied by many hundreds of merchant ships of all nations. These ships, however, are not always at sea, and when they are they constantly change position, so that reports from a particular ocean area vary in number from day to day. For the past twenty years a small fixed network has been provided by ships, specially equipped for comprehensive meteorological observing and occupying fixed positions in the North Atlantic and North Pacific. These are called **ocean weather ships**, and they report four or eight times daily as do the major land stations.

PHYSICAL FACTORS OF WEATHER
Temperature

The hotness or coldness of a substance is called its temperature, and is measured with a **thermometer**. The ordinary thermometer consists of a hollow glass bulb attached to a narrow stem with a thread-like bore. The bulb is filled with a liquid, usually mercury, which expands when the temperature rises and contracts when it falls, and this effect is made visible by the position of the end of thread of mercury in the stem. A scale of degrees is engraved on the stem for reading the temperature. Some kinds of thermometer have the scale engraved on a metal or wood mounting, but these are not suitable for meteorological purposes because the thermometer is liable to move on its mount. For measuring low temperatures another liquid, usually alcohol, is used, for mercury freezes at temperatures often reached in cold climates.

In meteorology it is the true air temperature that is important. A thermometer measures its own temperature — strictly the temperature of the liquid in the bulb, and unless certain precautions are taken this will not be the same as the temperature of the surrounding air. For example, if a thermometer is exposed to direct sunshine or even reflected sunshine from a nearby building it will indicate a temperature higher than the air temperature. Adequate ventilation of the

A meteorological screen shields the thermometer from radiation while allowing the air from outside to pass freely over it, thus giving true air temperature.

An ordinary thermometer

thermometer bulb is also necessary, for pockets of warm or cold air can form around the bulb and affect the reading. For these reasons meteorological thermometers are enclosed in a screen, usually a wooden box with louvred sides.

For measuring air temperature on expeditions and in confined spaces where normal equipment is unsuitable, special ventilated thermometers are used. A simple type is the whirling thermometer; it is mounted in a wooden frame which swivels on a handle (rather like a football fan's rattle). In a better type, the thermometer is mounted inside a polished metal tube and the air is drawn past it by a motor.

The **thermograph** is an instrument for providing a continuous record of the temperature on a strip of paper. A simple form of thermograph consists of a coiled strip of two different metals fused together. Unequal expansion of the two metals with temperature change causes the strip to wind or unwind. This movement is magnified by a long arm connected to the coil, which holds a pen that traces a record on a paper strip wrapped around a clockwork revolving drum.

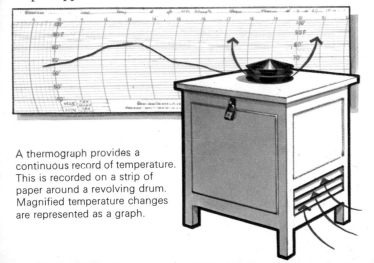

A thermograph provides a continuous record of temperature. This is recorded on a strip of paper around a revolving drum. Magnified temperature changes are represented as a graph.

Temperature scales are expressed in degrees of either Fahrenheit (° F) or Centigrade (° C). By international agreement the name Centigrade has been replaced by Celsius in official meteorology, but to all intents and purposes the scales are the same. A temperature scale is fixed firstly by two points, the freezing and boiling points of water. For the Centigrade scale the range between the two points is divided into 100 equal parts called degrees, and the numbers 0 and 100 were chosen to represent the freezing and boiling points. Temperatures below freezing are less than zero and must be expressed as negative numbers. On the Fahrenheit scale freezing point is 32° F and boiling point 212° F. The Fahrenheit degree is about one half (exactly, $\frac{5}{9}$) of the centigrade degree. The Centigrade scale is used by most world meteorological services.

For scientific purposes the **Absolute temperature** (° A) or Kelvin (° K) scale is used. The degree the same as the Centigrade degree; freezing point is 273° A and boiling point 373° A. The Absolute Zero is therefore —273° C and is the lowest temperature attainable in the physical universe.

Special thermometers are used to indicate **maximum and minimum temperatures**, the highest and lowest temperatures reached over a period, usually one day. The maximum thermometer has a constriction in the bore near the bulb. As the temperature rises the mercury is forced past the constriction, but when it begins to fall the mercury is held by the constriction at its highest point, as in a clinical thermometer. A minimum thermometer has alcohol as its working liquid. Immersed in the end of the thread of alcohol in the bore is a small metal index which is drawn back by the receding alcohol when the temperature falls and left in its lowest position when the temperature begins to rise again.

At night, especially when the sky is clear and the wind light, the temperature close to the ground falls several degrees below the air temperature. When the air temperature is above freezing and near the ground the temperature is below freezing, there is said to be a ground frost. An air frost occurs when the air temperature is also below freezing. Temperature near the ground is measured by exposing a **grass minimum thermometer** to the open sky on two short pegs so that it lies horizontally about $\frac{1}{2}$ inch above closely-cut grass.

Maximum thermometer
(Diagramatic)

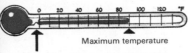

Maximum temperature

Mercury thread breaks at constriction as temperature falls. The thermometer is reset by shaking the mercury back into the bulb.

Minimum thermometer

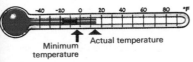

Minimum temperature — Actual temperature

Index is drawn back to minimum position as temperature falls. The thermometer is reset by tilting it, bulb end upwards.

Grass minimum thermometer

The most extreme air temperatures at the earth's surface are:
Highest: 136°F (57·8°C) at Aziza, Tripoli, September 1922 and San Luis, Mexico, August 1933.
Lowest: −127°F (−88·3°C) at Vostok, Antarctica, August 1960.

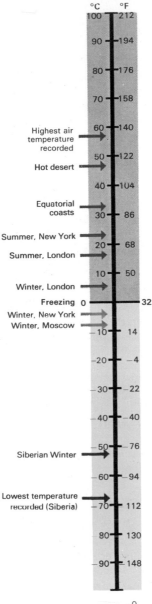

°C	°F	
100	212	
90	194	
80	176	
70	158	
60	140	← Highest air temperature recorded
50	122	
		← Hot desert
40	104	
30	86	← Equatorial coasts
		← Summer, New York
20	68	← Summer, London
10	50	
		← Winter, London
0	32	Freezing
		← Winter, New York
−10	14	← Winter, Moscow
−20	−4	
−30	−22	
−40	−40	
−50	−76	← Siberian Winter
−60	−94	
−70	−112	← Lowest temperature recorded (Siberia)
−80	−130	
−90	−148	

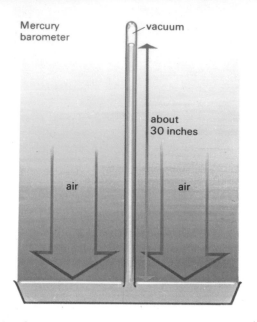

Mercury
barometer

vacuum

about
30 inches

air

air

Pressure

Like all fluids, the air exerts a pressure on everything within
and around it, although we are not so aware of it as we are of
temperature. The pressure of the air was, in fact, not realized
until the Italian scientist Torricelli carried out his famous
experiment in 1643. Torricelli took a straight narrow tube
with one end open, the other closed, filled it with mercury and
stood it upright with its open end submerged in a bowl of
mercury. A column of mercury about 30 inches high remained
standing in the tube, and this could happen only if the
atmosphere were pressing on the surface of the mercury in the
bowl.

Pressure is a force, or weight, evenly distributed over a
surface, and it is commonly expressed in pounds per square
inch. At the earth's surface the air pressure is about 14 lbs/sq.
in. or 2,000 lbs/sq. ft. This means that the weight of a column
of air one foot square extending from sea level to the outer
limit of the atmosphere is nearly one ton.

Atmospheric pressure is usually measured with a **mercury
barometer**, which, in principle is the simple apparatus used

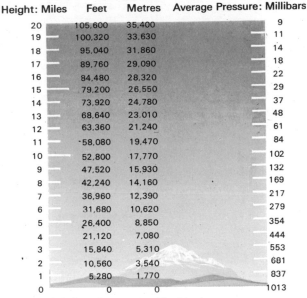

Height: Miles	Feet	Metres	Average Pressure: Millibars
20	105,600	35,400	9
19	100,320	33,630	11
18	95,040	31,860	14
17	89,760	29,090	18
16	84,480	28,320	22
15	79,200	26,550	29
14	73,920	24,780	37
13	68,640	23,010	48
12	63,360	21,240	61
11	58,080	19,470	84
10	52,800	17,770	102
9	47,520	15,930	132
8	42,240	14,160	169
7	36,960	12,390	217
6	31,680	10,620	279
5	26,400	8,850	354
4	21,120	7,080	444
3	15,840	5,310	553
2	10,560	3,540	681
1	5,280	1,770	837
0	0	0	1013

Variation of pressure with altitude

by Torricelli. His bowl of mercury is replaced by a small metal cistern firmly attached to the tube with only a small opening for the air – to make the instrument easy to handle without spilling the mercury. A scale is engraved on the tube for reading the height of the mercury column.

From the height of the mercury column and its density can be deduced the weight of an equal column one square inch in area, and therefore the pressure in pounds per square inch. **Barometer corrections** must be made for the temperature of the instrument, which affects both the density of the mercury and the length of the scale on the tube. With these corrections, pressure is commonly measured accurately to one part in 10,000.

In the household type of mercury barometer the cistern is replaced by a short length of the tube bent upwards at its lower open end. A float on the surface of the mercury moves up and down as the pressure changes and, by means of a cord, actuates a pointer, which moves over a dial marked to indicate the pressure.

The mercury barometer, at least 3 feet long is a cumbersome instrument and the **aneroid barometer** is a more compact type. Its essential part is a small capsule or concertina-like box, partially exhausted of air, which is squeezed or stretched as the atmospheric pressure rises or falls. The box is connected by a system of levers to a pointer, which, in conjunction with a dial, indicates the pressure. Although, generally speaking, the aneroid is less accurate than the mercury type, an extremely accurate and compact form of aneroid with an electronic indicator has been designed for meteorological use.

Pressure units are commonly expressed in inches (or millimetres) of mercury, the height of the mercury read directly from the barometer, although to obtain a true reading it is necessary to correct for the temperature of the barometer. In meteorological practice a true pressure unit is adopted; it is called the millibar and is equal to 1,000 dynes (1·02 grams weight) per square centimetre. At sea level the average pressure of the atmosphere is about 1,000 millibars (mb), but actual values vary from place to place and from hour to hour. Sea level pressures above 1,060 mb, or below 920 mb, are extremely rare, though 887 mb was once observed in a

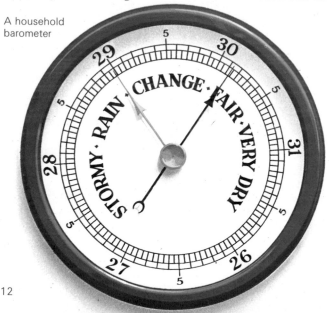

A household barometer

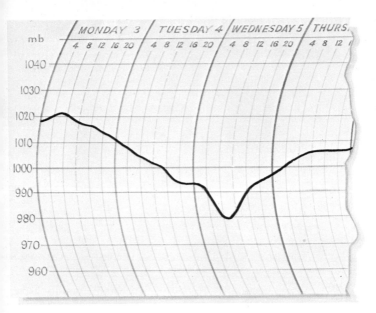

Part of the chart, barogram, from a recording barometer

tropical storm that occurred in the western Pacific.

The pressure at any place is that due to the weight of the air above it; therefore pressure becomes less with height. Mountaineers at high altitudes suffer from shortage of air, and high flying aircraft require pressurized cabins. Pressure is about half its surface value, 500 mb, at 18,000 feet, and one tenth of its surface value, 100 mb, at about 53,000 feet. For weather forecasting, pressures observed at the various stations must be adjusted to the same level, and this usually results in a **reduction of pressure to sea level**, although a higher level for adjustment is used in certain plateau areas, such as Central and East Africa. Near sea level, pressure falls by approximately 1 mb for each 30 feet of altitude.

An aircraft **altimeter** is a form of aneroid barometer. The dial reads the heights corresponding to the pressures at the various flying levels, but correction has to be made for vary-ing sea level pressure. For example, an altimeter at a pressure of 500 mb indicates a height of about 18,000 feet.

13

40°C 104°F	51g/cu
30°C 82°F	30g/cu
20°C 68°F	17g/cu
10°C 50°F	9g/cu.
0°C 32°F	5g/cu.
-10°C 14°F	2g/cu.

Variation of saturation with temperature

Humidity

Some water in the form of invisible vapour is intermixed with the air throughout the atmosphere. It is the condensation of this vapour which gives rise to most weather phenomena – clouds, rain, snow, fog and dew for example; for this reason an understanding of the atmospheric water vapour is of great importance in weather study. The amount of water vapour in the air is most simply expressed as the weight in a specified volume of air, for example, grams per cubic metre.

There is a limit to the amount of water vapour which a given volume of air can hold and when the air holds this limiting amount it is said to be **saturated**. Warm air can hold more vapour than cold air; for each degree rise of temperature there is a rise in the water vapour content for saturation, and this rise per degree increases as the temperature increases.

In general the air is not saturated; it contains only a fraction of the possible water vapour. This fraction, expressed as a percentage, is called the **relative humidity**. For example, air at 50° F, if saturated, contains 9·4 gr/cu m of water vapour and the relative humidity is 100%. If it contains only half this amount, 4·7 gr/cu m the relative humidity is 50%. If the relative humidity is low the air is said to be dry, and it then feels brisk and invigorating; if the relative humidity is high the air is moist or damp; in summer it feels relaxing, sultry or oppressive, and in winter muggy or raw.

If unsaturated air is cooled it will eventually reach a temperature at which it will be saturated. Any further cooling leads to condensation of the excess vapour. This is seen when the warm moist breath of passengers gives rise to misting on motor car windows on a cold day. The temperature at which condensation sets in is called the **dew point**, and car window misting occurs because the temperature of the glass is lower than the dew point of the air inside the car.

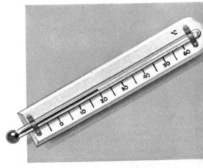

Neither the weight of water vapour per cubic metre of air, nor the dew point, are easy to measure except under laboratory conditions. It is more convenient to use comparisons between the dry bulb thermometer *(above)* and wet bulb thermometer *(right)*. The difference between these can be converted into relative humidity. When the air is saturated, no evaporation takes place from the wet bulb and it reads the same as the dry. The lower the humidity the greater the difference between the bulbs. Normally the wet bulb temperature lies between the dry bulb and the dew point.

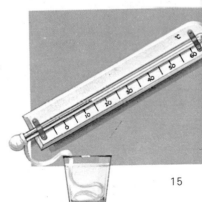

At a weather observing station, where the humidity has to be assessed several times a day, a **wet bulb thermometer** is used. This is an ordinary thermometer which has its bulb covered closely with a little muslin bag, from which a wick of absorbent material dips into a small vessel containing pure water. The water passes up the wick to the muslin and then evaporates, cooling the thermometer bulb. The wet bulb temperature is therefore in general lower than the air temperature (indicated by the ordinary or **dry bulb thermometer**). This difference can, with the aid of humidity tables, be translated into relative humidity, water vapour content, or dew point.

The process of evaporation absorbs a very large amount of heat. When water reaches boiling point its temperature does not rise any more but the heat is all consumed in boiling away, that is evaporating the water. It takes nearly six times as much heat to evaporate a quantity of water as it does to heat it from freezing to boiling. If the vapour subsequently condenses the same amount of heat is given out. The heat involved in these processes, which are not accompanied by any change of

Water vapour content of air at various relative humidities

Temperature	Water vapour content grams per cubic metre				
	59·3	34·0	18·7	9·8	4·9
140°F (40°C)	100%	57%	31%	17%	8%
86°F (30°C)	•	100%	55%	29%	14%
68°F (20°C)	•	•	100%	52%	26%
50°F (10°C)	•	•	•	100%	50%
32°F (0°C)	•	•	•	•	100%

Weather house

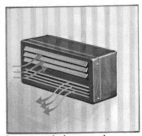

Convected air central heating radiator

Water at 32°F, if heated to 212°F, uses this much heat

Water at 212°F, if changed to steam, uses this much heat

temperature, is called **latent heat**. Freezing and melting also involve latent heat. It takes $\frac{4}{5}$ as much to melt ice with its temperature steady at $0°$ C as it does to heat the resulting water from $0°$ C to $100°$ C. If water freezes latent heat is released.

These concepts explain forms of **primitive air conditioning**. In cold climates the outside air, even if saturated, can hold only a small amount of water vapour. When drawn into a heated building (ventilation), it is warmed up but remains very dry – hence the unpleasant effects of powerful central heating. These effects can be mitigated by providing water for evaporating. To be really effective, however, these methods require the evaporation of substantial amounts of water; this consumes latent heat and cools the air. Modern air conditioning plants control these processes mechanically, but the principles are the same.

The upper air

This book has so far dealt with conditions in the thin layer at the bottom of the atmosphere. Now it is necessary to consider the third dimension, height, because the more important weather processes like cloud, rain and snow formation take place in the upper air, some one to six miles above the surface.

The **composition of the atmosphere** is a mixture of gases; the main constituents are nitrogen (about 78%) and oxygen (21%), and there are small quantities of various other gases of which the inert gas argon is the chief. The proportions of these gases are remarkably constant all over the world up to a height of about 45 miles but there are also two main variable constituents, water vapour and carbon-dioxide. The amount of water vapour is constantly changing by evaporation and condensation. Carbon dioxide is increased by the burning of fuels and decreased by being absorbed by green vegetation, and dissolved in the sea; these processes balance one another and the amount of carbon dioxide in the air alters very little. Water vapour is much more important in weather processes.

Upper air observations of temperature and humidity were first measured by recording instruments, carried up on kites or tethered balloons, but these were limited to heights of one or two miles. Later, free balloons, reaching six miles, were used. but were successful only if the records were subsequently recovered. At a later period aircraft were used, carrying dry and wet bulb thermometers mounted on the wings, but this method involved a flight to high levels for each sounding.

The modern instrument for measuring upper air conditions is the **radio-sonde**. It is essentially a small radio transmitter

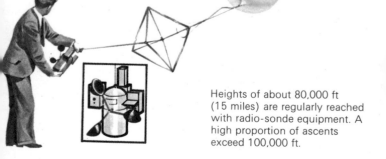

Heights of about 80,000 ft (15 miles) are regularly reached with radio-sonde equipment. A high proportion of ascents exceed 100,000 ft.

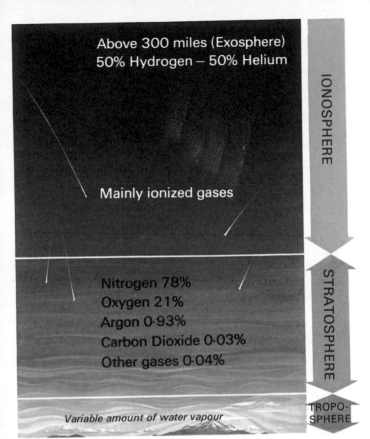

Above 300 miles (Exosphere)
50% Hydrogen – 50% Helium

IONOSPHERE

Mainly ionized gases

STRATOSPHERE

Nitrogen 78%
Oxygen 21%
Argon 0·93%
Carbon Dioxide 0·03%
Other gases 0·04%

TROPO-
SPHERE

Variable amount of water vapour

Composition of the atmosphere; variation with height

with three circuits connected to devices which respond to temperature, humidity and pressure. It is carried up on a free balloon. A small windmill, turned by the motion of the balloon through the air, switches in each circuit in turn for a few seconds. Changes in the upper air conditions cause changes in the radio frequencies emmitted by the three circuits. The frequencies are measured at the receiving station on the ground and translated into temperature, humidity or pressure as appropriate. This observation is now carried out twice daily at stations all over the world, including the ocean weather ships.

19

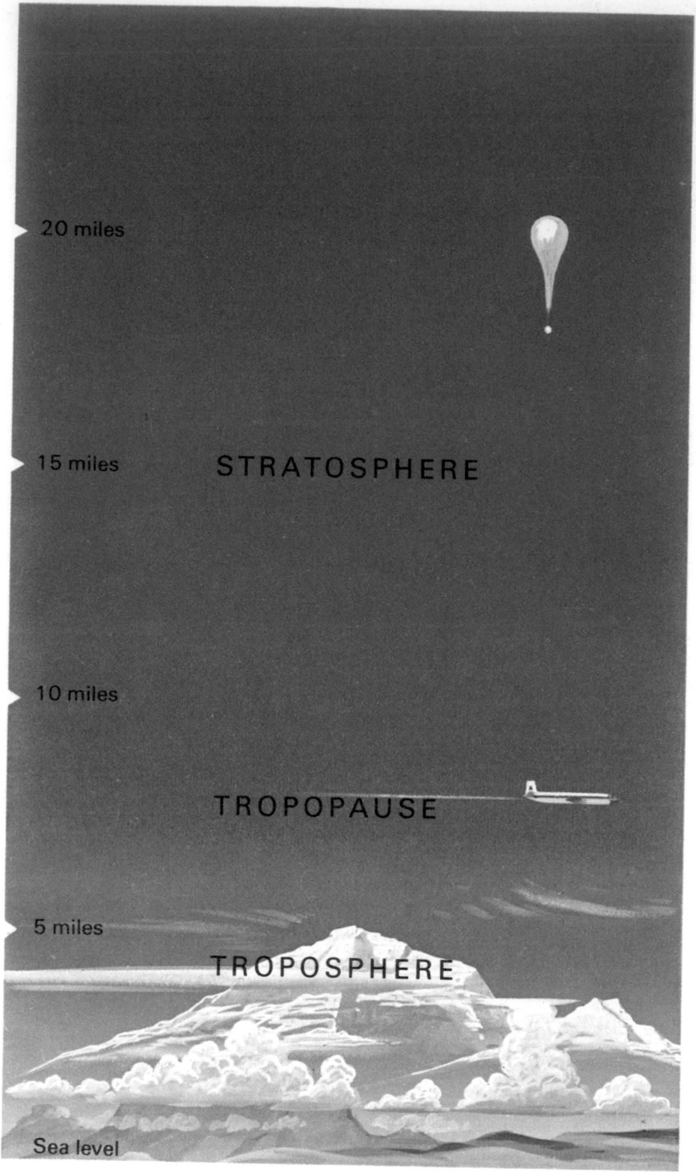

20 miles

15 miles   STRATOSPHERE

10 miles

  TROPOPAUSE

5 miles

TROPOSPHERE

Sea level

On average the temperature at the top of a 5,000 foot mountain is about 9° C (16° F) lower than at its foot, and this fall of temperature takes place gradually with increase of altitude. Measurements in the upper air by the methods described on pages 18 and 19 show that the fall of temperature aloft is world-wide. However, it does not go on indefinitely; a level is reached at which the temperature stops falling, and above that level it becomes steady to beyond the greatest heights reached by radio-sondes, about 20 miles. The lower region where increase of height is accompanied by decrease of temperature (3° F per 1,000 feet) is called the **troposphere**. In it take place the activities of the atmosphere which we call weather, for example cloud and rain formation. The upper region, cloud-free with steady temperature, is called the **stratosphere**. The boundary between the two regions is called the **tropopause**. The height of the tropopause varies daily but generally it is highest near the Equator (about 11 miles) and descends towards the poles (about 4 miles).

The fall of temperature with height in the troposphere is referred to as a lapse: the rate of fall, which may be expressed in degrees per 1,000 feet or per kilometre, is called the **lapse rate**. Unsaturated air changes temperature by $5\frac{1}{2}$° F per 1,000 feet of ascent or descent (1° C per 100 metres). This particular value is called the **dry adiabatic lapse rate**, meaning the air exchanges no heat with its surroundings, a condition very nearly true for rising and descending packets of air.

The lapse rate expresses the fall of temperature in relation to height

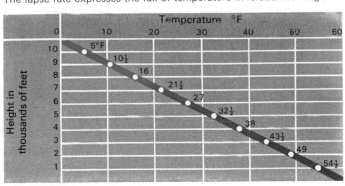

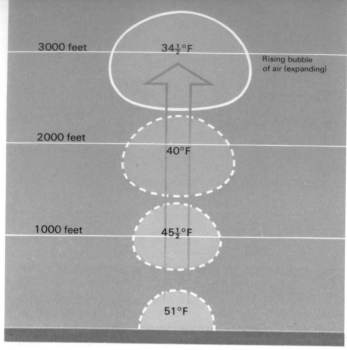

3000 feet	$34\frac{1}{2}°F$
	Rising bubble of air (expanding)
2000 feet	$40°F$
1000 feet	$45\frac{1}{2}°F$
	$51°F$

Temperature changes in rising unsaturated air

Stability and instability

When a packet of air near the earth's surface becomes slightly heated, it will begin to rise, being lighter than the surrounding air. Whether or not it will go on rising depends upon how the temperature in the surrounding air changes with height. Suppose for example that the air temperature near the ground is $50°$ F and at 1,000 feet, $44°$ F. If the packet of air is warmed to $51°$ F it will begin to rise; its temperature will fall at $5\frac{1}{2}°$ F per 1,000 feet, and therefore when it reaches 1,000 feet its temperature will be $51°$ less $5\frac{1}{2}°$, that is $45\frac{1}{2}°$ F. It will be warmer by $1\frac{1}{2}°$ F than the surrounding air at the same level, and it will therefore continue to rise. The atmosphere in these circumstances is said to be **unstable**, because a packet of air, once it begins to rise will continue to do so. This occurs because the lapse rate in the atmosphere is greater than the dry adiabatic, $5\frac{1}{2}°$ F per 1,000 feet (page 21). Now suppose that the lapse rate is less than dry adiabatic, for example that the

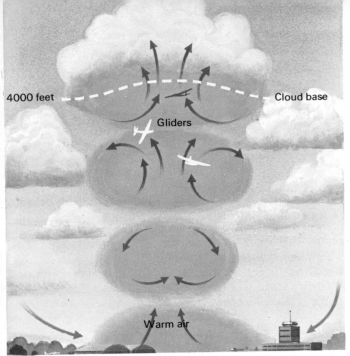

4000 feet

Cloud base

Gliders

Warm air

Glider pilots seek out continuously rising air currents, or thermals

temperature at 1,000 feet is 47° F. The rising packet of air at 1,000 feet, temperature 45½° F is now colder and therefore heavier than the surrounding air, and it will fall back to its original position. In this case the atmosphere is said to be **stable**. The dry adiabatic lapse rate is therefore critical in the sense that if in the atmosphere this lapse rate is exceeded rising and falling motion of packets of air is sustained; otherwise it is suppressed.

If the heating of the air near the surface is maintained, for example by the sun heating a patch of dry bare earth, there will result not a single packet of rising air but a continuous upward current. Such currents, called **thermals**, are well known to glider pilots, who seek them out because of their power to maintain or increase the glider's height. A more common effect of thermals can be seen in the continued soaring of birds when they remain airborne with their wings spread motionless.

When the air is saturated the processes are similar to those described for dry air on pages 22 and 23, but the amount of temperature change is different. A rising packet of saturated air will immediately begin to cool, on expansion, but the cooling will cause condensation, releasing latent heat (page 16). Consequently the **temperature in rising moist air** falls less than it otherwise would. For air at ordinary temperatures the cooling is about 3° F per 1,000 feet. For very warm saturated air the rate of cooling is somewhat less, and for very cold air, which has little water vapour available for condensation the cooling rate is almost the same as for dry air, $5\frac{1}{2}$° F per 1,000 feet.

The arguments regarding stability and instability for dry air (pages 22 and 23) may be repeated for rising saturated air except that the critical lapse rate is different; its average value is 3° F per 1,000 feet. This is called the **saturated adiabatic lapse rate.** For descending saturated air however the initial slight warming causes the air to become unsaturated; it then behaves as dry air, its temperature rising at $5\frac{1}{2}$° F per 1,000 feet.

If the packet of rising air is unsaturated it will, to begin with, behave like rising dry air. But at some stage it will be cooled to its dew point (page 14), and thereafter behave like saturated air. That is what usually happens in the atmosphere. The moisture condensing out of the rising cooling air becomes visible as a cloud, usually Cumulus, the cloud type with a flat base and rounded cauliflower-like heads (page 53). These clouds are useful to glider pilots because they mark the tops of thermals and the pilots do not have to search for them. If the upward current goes on rising to very great heights the result becomes the towering Cumulonimbus or thundercloud (page 53).

It sometimes happens that the temperature in the atmosphere increases upwards through a limited layer, which may rest on the surface or occur at some upper level. This is an **inversion**, an extremely stable state, and it very strongly damps out any tendency for rising or descending air currents.

When rising moist air reaches its condensation level the cooling air becomes visible as a cloud, usually Cumulus, with a flat base.

Wind

The air is nearly always in motion, and this is felt as wind. Two factors are necessary to specify wind, its direction and force, or speed. The direction is usually expressed as that point of the compass from which the wind blows, thus, north, southeast, west-southwest. It is also expressed in degrees from true north, thus, N, 0° or 360°, E, 90°, S, 180° and W, 270°. The speed is expressed in miles per hour, knots, metres per second, and so on, or as force on the Beaufort Scale, (pages 28 and 29).

In popular weather lore, winds from the various directions have their own particular qualities, illustrated in the British Isles by the old rhymes:—

The north wind doth blow, and we shall have snow . . .

and

When the wind is in the east, 'tis neither fit for man nor beast.

These express the unpleasant characters of the north and east winds in winter and spring, which arise because these winds come from the cold northern seas or the cold continent of Europe. They do not necessarily apply to other parts of the world. On the eastern seaboard of the United States for

A wind vane used for observing wind direction must have an open exposure, unobstructed by trees or buildings which can cause local eddies and give quite a false indication.

Strong prevailing winds leave their mark on the countryside in the form of bent and distorted trees, familar sights in coast and hill areas.

example, in winter, easterly winds from the ocean may well be warmer than westerlies off the cold continent. In Australia, northerlies are hot winds from the tropics. What is important is the terrain over which the wind has travelled during the past day or two.

The **prevailing wind** direction at any place is that which occurs most often. Over much of western Europe and North America it is westerly; in the Caribbean and Tropics generally it is easterly. The prevailing wind does not blow continually; other directions occur for a substantial part of the time. The wind is never steady, but blows in a series of gusts and lulls. Gusts last only a few seconds, and though they give rise to the highest wind speeds a more realistic measure of wind speed is its average over a longer period. Some extremes of recorded wind speeds are (in gusts), Mt. Washington, United States, 231 mph, and Jan Mayen, 188 mph.

At a given temperature the air feels cooler if there is a wind than if it is calm; the stronger the wind the greater is its cooling power. At low temperatures this effect is called **wind chill**. Temperatures far below freezing are tolerable in calm weather, but can be lethal in strong winds.

In desert regions, the prevailing wind is responsible for the alignment and shaping of sand-dunes.

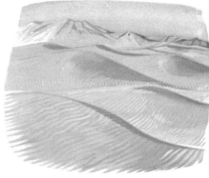

Temperatures of 27°–32°F (−3°–0°C) in calm conditions give rise to only slight frost, but, if the wind is strong the frost is severe and penetrating.

Force	0	1	2	3	4	F
Description	Calm	Light air	Light breeze	Gentle breeze	Moderate	
Effect						
Weather symbol						

Many, but not all, official weather observing stations are equipped with instruments for measuring wind speed. The **Beaufort scale of wind force** enables the speed to be estimated without instrumental aid, by the effects of the wind on common objects, and is a great help to amateur observers. The scale was devised in the nineteenth century by a British sailor, Admiral Sir Francis Beaufort. Originally it was intended for observing winds at sea by their effects on sailing ships and the wave appearance. It has been adapted for use on land in relation to the effects of wind on smoke, trees and buildings.

Specification of the Beaufort Scale

Force No.	Effects
0	Calm, smoke rises vertically.
1	Direction of wind shown by smoke drift, but not by vane.

7	8	9	10	11	12
Moderate gale	Gale	Strong gale	Whole gale	–	–

Diagrammatic representation of the Beaufort scale

2	Wind felt on face, leaves rustle; ordinary vane moved by wind.
3	Leaves and small twigs in constant motion; wind extends light flag.
4	Raises dust and loose paper; small branches are moved.
5	Small trees in leaf begin to sway; crested wavelets form on inland waters.
6	Large branches in motion; whistling heard in telegraph wires; umbrellas used with difficulty.
7	Whole trees in motion; inconvenience felt when walking against wind.
8	Breaks twigs off trees; generally impedes progress.
9	Slight structural damage occurs; chimney pots and slates removed.
10	Seldom experienced inland; trees uprooted; considerable structural damage occurs.
11 & 12	Very rarely experienced; widespread damage occurs.

The instruments used for measuring wind speed are called anemometers. The simplest form is the **cup anemometer**, a set of three or four bowl- or conical-shaped vanes about the size of a tea cup, mounted on arms which rotate on a vertical spindle. A counting device can be used to indicate the number of revolutions in a given time interval, say ten seconds, or one minute, and from this number the wind speed may be obtained by reference to a table supplied with the instrument. In modern instruments the wind speed is indicated on a dial which resembles some forms of car speedometer. The connection between the anemometer and the indicator dial is often electrical, so that the dial may be set up indoors some distance from the anemometer. This arrangement is used in control towers on airfields.

An older type of instrument is the **pressure-tube anemometer**. It consists of a wind vane in the form of a hollow tube, the open end of which always points into wind. An increase of wind causes an increase of pressure in the vane, which is communicated to the indicator by a tube leading down the mast. The changes are translated into variations of wind speed.

The wind is always turbulent to a greater or less degree, that is, its speed constantly varies in gusts and lulls, each lasting a few seconds. Obstructions such as buildings and trees are one cause of **turbulence**, but an equally important cause is atmospheric instability (page 22). If the air is unstable, vertical motion takes place freely; slow moving packets of air rise away from the surface and are replaced by rapidly moving packets coming down. This interchange gives rise to **gustiness**. If the air is stable vertical motion tends to be damped out, and the wind is smoother.

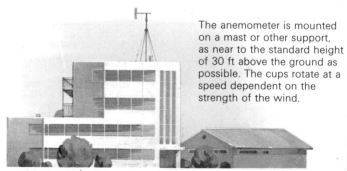

The anemometer is mounted on a mast or other support, as near to the standard height of 30 ft above the ground as possible. The cups rotate at a speed dependent on the strength of the wind.

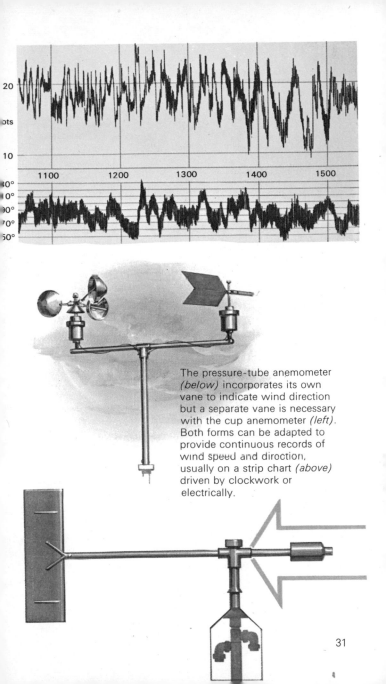

The pressure-tube anemometer *(below)* incorporates its own vane to indicate wind direction but a separate vane is necessary with the cup anemometer *(left)*. Both forms can be adapted to provide continuous records of wind speed and direction, usually on a strip chart *(above)* driven by clockwork or electrically.

31

Pilot balloon theodolite *(left)* and balloon and radar reflector *(above)*

Winds in the upper air

Winds at levels well above the surface are important not only in weather processes but also for the navigation of aircraft; and routine observations of upper winds have been made at a selection of stations for many years. Before the Second World War the observations were made almost always by means of **pilot balloons.**

Nowadays upper winds are measured by means of **radar** (page 102). A radar reflector made of metal foil is carried up by a radio-sonde balloon (page 18), and 'followed' by a radar set on the ground. The radar points at the reflector, thus determining its bearing and angular elevation continuously throughout the flight; it also determines the slant distance of the balloon. These three quantities determine the track of the balloon, and hence the winds at all levels to the highest reached, or until the balloon passes out of range of the radar. In the most modern method the radar follows the balloon automatically, and a small electronic computer works out the winds while the flight is in progress. Winds of up to 100,000 feet, which is a height of nearly 20 miles, are regularly observed by this method, whereas pilot balloon observations are limited by the heights of cloud layers in which the balloon disappears.

Pilot balloons are made of rubber and about 2 ft in diameter. These are filled with hydrogen so that, supporting a standard weight, it will rise at 500 ft per minute. The balloon is followed with a special theodolite. At each minute after its release the angle of the balloon above the horizon is read. The height of the balloon is 500 ft × the number of minutes since release. Together with the two angles this fixes the balloon position relative to the observer and thus, direction and distance. This gives the wind in the layer between the two levels reached by the balloon at the beginning and end of each minute.

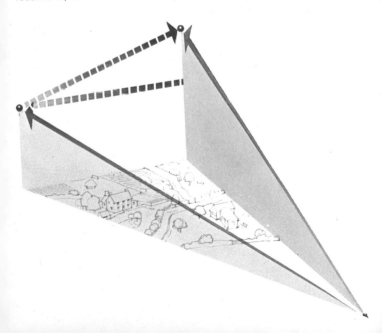

Winds show considerable **variation** between the upper and lower atmosphere. In the lowest layers of the atmosphere, up to about 2,000 feet above the surface, the wind speed usually increases upwards. It is well known, for example, that winds are stronger around the tops of tall buildings than over the neighbouring ground. The reason is that near the ground the air flow is slowed by friction. But this effect depends on the lapse rate (page 21); if the air is unstable, fast moving air from aloft moves freely down to the surface, increasing the wind there; this happens on sunny and showery days. If the air is stable the fast moving air remains aloft, and the surface wind is often quite light, as in a fog, or at night if the sky is clear of clouds.

If the wind blows broadside on to a long mountain range it tends to follow the terrain, rising on the windward slope and descending on the lee. The windward slopes are therefore much used for gliding, but the downward current on the lee side is sometimes dangerous to light aircraft and may force them down to ground level, with disastrous consequences. A train of such waves may be set up downwind of the mountain, and these waves may occur up to levels far above summit of the range.

At levels above about 2,000 feet the winds usually increase upwards to near the tropopause (page 20). They are important to modern aircraft, which may encounter head winds of 100 knots or more at cruising levels.

Variation of wind with height. Near the ground it is checked by friction.

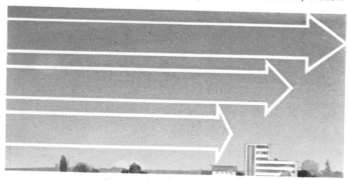

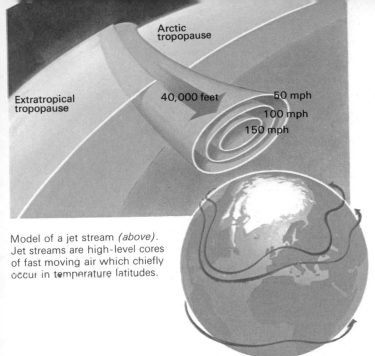

Model of a jet stream *(above)*.
Jet streams are high-level cores
of fast moving air which chiefly
occur in temperature latitudes.

The most prominent features of high-level winds are the **jet streams** – ribbons or cores of very fast moving air in which speeds of over 100 knots, occasionally 200 knots may be reached. Sharp differences of temperature occur across jet streams; in the northern hemisphere the warmer lies to the right of the jet and in the southern hemisphere to the left. The main jet streams occur in temperate latitudes, and pursue a wavy course round the globe in each hemisphere, with the air flow from west to east. They occur near the tropopause, at 30,000 to 40,000 feet, are limited to a few thousand feet in depth and to some tens of miles horizontally. Other jets occur in winter in the sub-tropics, for example, North Africa and northern India, and in summer there is an easterly jet over northern India. In the stratosphere in winter in high latitudes there is a westerly jet, known as the Polar Night Jet, but it is too high to affect present day aircraft. The jet streams change their positions from day to day. In the stratosphere the winds decrease upwards, and by the 100,000 feet level they have usually become quite light.

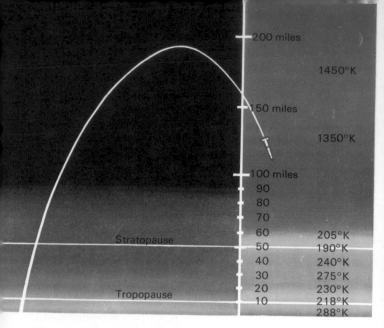

200 miles	
	1450°K
150 miles	
	1350°K
100 miles	
90	
80	
70	
Stratopause 60	205°K
50	190°K
40	240°K
30	275°K
Tropopause 20	230°K
10	218°K
	288°K

Very high atmosphere

The atmosphere has been systematically explored up to a height of about 100,000 feet, mainly by means of radio-sondes (page 18). Above this level our knowledge of the high atmosphere is scanty, obtained by means of rockets and satellites, and from observations of the aurora and meteorites. Meteorological rockets can be fired to heights of about 80 miles. Besides carrying devices for sampling the atmosphere chemically, they also eject radio-sondes, which fall attached to parachutes, and measure the temperature and pressure at high levels. Satellites orbit the earth at distances between 100 and 400 miles.

The atmosphere thins out gradually upwards, but it has no definite outer limit; it fades away so to speak. Up to about 50 miles its chemical composition remains the same as at the surface (page 18), but above this level the oxygen and nitrogen gradually diminish, until at 500 miles and higher the atmosphere consists of the light gases, hydrogen and helium, in about equal proportions.

The two lowest layers, the troposphere and stratosphere were discussed on page 20. In the low stratosphere the temperature does not change much with height, but higher up it increases, reaching a maximum at about 30 miles. From 30 to 50 miles the temperature falls again; this layer is called the **mesosphere**.

Between about 50 and 200 miles up there are a number of layers consisting of ionized gases (electrified molecules). These layers are called the **ionosphere**. They have the important property of reflecting radio waves, bending them downwards to turn with the curved surface of the earth. This makes possible the transmission of radio between distant places on the earth's surface.

Between about 30 and 50 miles there is a layer of ozone – a form of oxygen in which the molecule consists of three atoms instead of the normal two. Ozone is formed from ordinary oxygen by the action of ultra-violet light in the sun's rays. These rays, if they penetrated to the earth's surface would be harmful to life, and probably lethal. Fortunately the ozone absorbs these rays, screening the lower atmosphere. Were it not for this screening, life on earth could not exist in its present form.

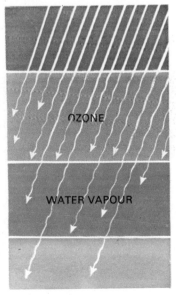

(Left) composition and temperature variations of the very high atmosphere

The ozone layer lies 30 to 50 miles above the earth's surface and is formed from ultra-violet light in the sun's rays. If these rays penetrated to the earth they would be lethal.

Radiation

The 'first cause' of weather is the radiation received from the Sun. Radiation consists of electro-magnetic waves which take many forms. It travels at the speed of light, 300,000 kilometres (186,000 miles) per second. Light from the Sun, at a distance of 93 million miles takes about eight minutes to reach the Earth. The type of radiation may be expressed either by the wave length, that is, the distance between successive crests, or by the frequency, the number of waves per second. The frequency multiplied by the wave length is equal to the speed of light. The published radio and television programmes, and radio receivers, give the wave lengths or the frequencies, for tuning purposes. The various forms of radiation in order of wave length from short to long are X-rays, light, heat, television and VHF radio, and ordinary radio; these constitute the spectrum of electro-magnetic waves. Meteorology is concerned with the visible spectrum and the wave lengths which lie immediately on either side of it, the ultra-violet and the infra-red.

Sunlight is composed of the colours of the rainbow. The wave lengths are expressed in microns (one millionth part of a metre), and for light ranging from 0·4 microns for the violet,

Spectrum of electromagnetic waves

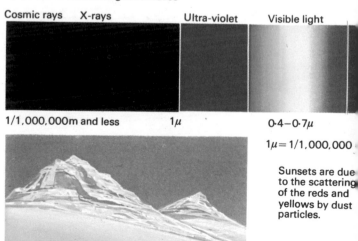

| Cosmic rays | X-rays | Ultra-violet | Visible light |

1/1,000,000m and less   1μ 0·4–0·7μ

$1\mu = 1/1,000,000$

Sunsets are due to the scattering of the reds and yellows by dust particles.

Snow reflects radiation.

through blue, green, yellow and orange, to 0·7 for the red.

When a body radiates, there is a wave length for which the energy is greatest, falling off for the wave lengths on either side. The higher the temperature of the body the shorter the wave length corresponding to maximum energy. For the Sun, this wave length is about 0·5 microns (blue-green light), corresponding to a temperature of about 6,000° C. Like all material bodies the Earth also radiates; its average temperature is about 15° C so that its maximum energy wave length is 10 microns, invisible, but detectable as heat.

Material bodies interact with radiation in various ways. They may be transparent, like glass or pure air, in which case the radiation passes through them with little or no effect on them. They may absorb the radiation; dark coloured objects are good absorbers, and as a result they become heated. Polished surfaces and snow reflect most of the radiation falling on them, and this leaves their temperature little affected. Dust in the atmosphere scatters the radiation giving a diffuse glow similar to that from car headlights in a fog. The blue of the sky is due to the scattering of the blue part of sunlight by air molecules, the reds and yellows of sunset to scattering by dust particles.

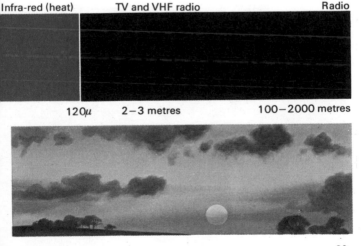

Infra-red (heat)   TV and VHF radio   Radio

120μ   2–3 metres   100–2000 metres

The Sun radiates energy at a rate which, for practical purposes, is unchanging. At the outer limit, the **radiation in the atmosphere** is 1·35 kilowatts per square metre of surface perpendicular to the beam; this is called the Solar Constant. Passing through the atmosphere it is depleted in various ways.

If the air is free from clouds, dust and smoke, it absorbs very little of the solar radiation, which passes directly to the Earth's surface, where it is partly absorbed and partly reflected. The absorbed part is used in heating the surface; that is why objects in sunshine become hot. Thus the atmosphere is heated not by the solar rays passing through it, but by the warmed Earth's surface, as a pan of water on a stove.

The Sun's radiation is referred to as short wave, and the radiation emitted by the Earth as long wave (page 39). The long wave radiation does not, however, pass freely through the air; part of it is absorbed, especially by water vapour and carbon dioxide. This warms the air, which in turn radiates some of the heat back to Earth, and some to space. Thus the atmosphere, by trapping some of the outgoing radiation, keeps the Earth's surface warmer than it would otherwise be; this is known as the 'Greenhouse Effect'. The Moon, having no atmosphere, is subject to extremely low temperatures in the parts not in sunshine. The energy of the radiation emitted by a body increases with its temperature; thus a warm surface loses heat by radiation more quickly than a cold one.

Clouds reflect much of the radiation which falls on them; if the cloud cover is thick and complete only about one tenth of the radiation gets through to the Earth's surface, as diffuse daylight. If, however, the cloud is broken, a particular spot may receive the direct solar beam and some radiation reflected from clouds as well, resulting in a higher temperature than if no clouds were present. The radiation outgoing from the Earth's surface is also partly reflected back by clouds, contributing to the greenhouse effect.

Absorption rates of different surfaces: 1. Water absorbs 60–90% of sunlight, depending on the angle of the Sun in the sky. 2. Dry sand 75%. 3. Ploughed field 75–95%. 4. Snow 25%. 5. Grassy field 80–90%. 6. Dense forest 95%

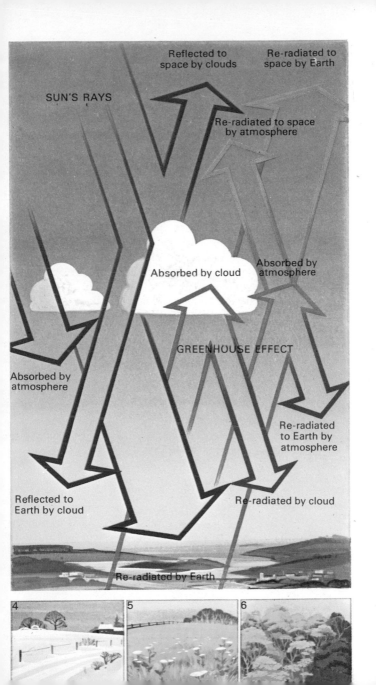

Reflected to space by clouds

Re-radiated to space by Earth

SUN'S RAYS

Re-radiated to space by atmosphere

Absorbed by cloud

Absorbed by atmosphere

GREENHOUSE EFFECT

Absorbed by atmosphere

Re-radiated to Earth by atmosphere

Reflected to Earth by cloud

Re-radiated by cloud

Re-radiated by Earth

4

5

6

Daily variations of weather factors

The daily cycle of sunshine and darkness gives rise to corresponding variations in the elements of weather. An obvious consequence is that night is, as a rule, colder than the daytime, but the daily cycle of **temperature** is not quite so simple as this might suggest. Radiation is received from the Sun during the period from sunrise to sunset, yet the temperature does not go on increasing all day; it reaches its highest value in the early afternoon, then decreases. This happens in spite of the fact that at 3 pm, say, the Sun is just as high in the sky as it was at 9 am, and then the temperature was rising. The reason is that the Earth's surface is constantly losing heat by radiation; the higher the temperature the greater the rate of loss. In the early afternoon the Earth's radiation begins to outweigh that received from the Sun, so that cooling sets in. It continues throughout the evening and night, the lowest temperature being reached at about sunrise.

The foregoing applies to land areas when the sky is clear. If there is a layer of cloud, both the incoming and outgoing radiation are restricted; the same kind of temperature cycle occurs but it is less pronounced, the days being cooler and the nights warmer. Clear nights in winter have sharp frosts; cloudy nights are, as a rule, less cold. Over the sea the difference between day and night temperatures is much less than over land. This is because the Sun's rays penetrate and

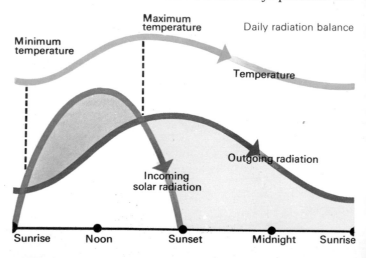

Minimum temperature

Maximum temperature

Daily radiation balance

Temperature

Outgoing radiation

Incoming solar radiation

Sunrise   Noon   Sunset   Midnight   Sunrise

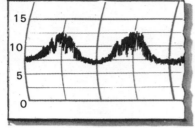

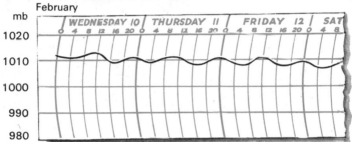

Normal daily wind record *(left)* showing freshening of wind during the daytime. *(Below)* tropical barogram illustrating the twice-daily cycle of pressure change.

spread their heating through a considerable depth of water. The movement of the water also spreads the heating, instead of restricting it to a thin surface layer, as on land.

Relative humidity, being to a large extent controlled by temperature tends to be low in the middle of the day and high at night – hence the greater drying power of the air by day, especially on warm days.

It was mentioned on page 34 that the surface **wind** is largely controlled by the interchange of fast moving upper air with air, slowed down by friction, near the surface. This interchange is most vigorous when the lapse rate is unstable, that is, when the surface air is warmest. It explains the well known tendency, in fine weather, for the wind to freshen by day, and to die away in the evening and night.

In the tropics there is a regular twice-daily cycle of **pressure** changes, with maxima at about 10 am and 10 pm and minima at 4 am and 4 pm, local time. The total variation amounts to 2 or 3 millibars. Outside the tropics this variation is barely detectable, being swamped by the much greater irregularities caused by depressions and anticyclones (pages 86 to 91).

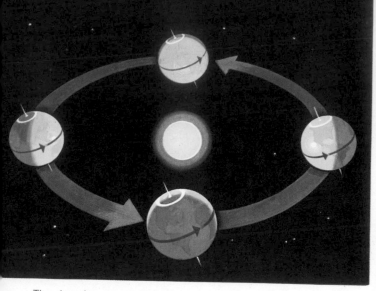

The changing aspect of the Earth, relative to the Sun produces the solstices and equinoxes.

The changing seasons with their varying lengths of day and night, and differing types of weather, arise from the changing aspect of the Earth, relative to the Sun, in its yearly revolution. The Earth's axis always points in the same direction in space, inclined at an angle of $66\frac{1}{2}°$ to the plane of the Earth's orbit. In winter (northern hemisphere) the North Pole is tilted away from the Sun, and at the winter solstice (December 22nd) all places within the Arctic Circle, latitude $66\frac{1}{2}°$ N, the Sun is not above the horizon at any time during the 24 hours. All other places in the northern hemisphere then have their shortest day. At the summer solstice, June 21, places within the Arctic Circle have 24 hours daylight, and all other places in the northern hemisphere then have their longest day. The seasons are reversed in the southern hemisphere. The varying aspect of the Earth relative to the Sun also accounts for the midday sun being higher in the sky in summer than in winter; the difference between midsummer and midwinter is 47°. This means that in summer, for several hours in the middle of the day, the Sun's rays strike the Earth at a more direct angle than in winter; their heating effect, being spread over a smaller area, is consequently greatest in summer. The longer days and the more nearly vertical solar rays account for the high summer temperatures compared with those of winter. This applies chiefly to land areas, especially the continental interiors of Canada and Siberia, where occasionally temperatures of 80° F are reached, even within the Arctic Circle, areas which in the winter are frozen hard.

The oceans respond much less, and more slowly, to the Sun's radiation and consequently, compared with neighbouring land areas, they are cooler in summer and warmer in winter. This explains, therefore, the tempering effect of the oceans on the adjacent land, where the prevailing winds are onshore; thus the western parts of North America and Europe have cooler summers and warmer winters as compared with continental interiors in the same latitudes.

Snow covered surfaces, being white, reflect away a large part of the solar radiation, and consequently derive little warming from it. Hence, in spite of the polar regions receiving considerably more radiation on a day in midsummer than many other parts of the Earth's surface, their snow cover remains permanent.

Annual temperature variation for selected places

Degrees F	Warm (summer)	Cold (winter)
London	64°F 18°C	40°F 4°C
Rome	76°F 25°C	44°F 7°C
Moscow	65°F 19°C	15°F −9°C
Nairobi	67°F 19°C	60°F 16°C
Johannesburg	68°F 20°C	50°F 10°C
New York	74°F 24°C	31°F −1°C
San Francisco	62°F 17°C	50°F 10°C
Bombay	85°F 29°C	75°F 24°C
Sydney	71°F 21°C	53°F 11°C
Wellington (N.Z.)	62°F 17°C	47°F 8°C

WEATHER CONDITIONS

Sunshine

Most weather observing stations, including, for obvious reasons, those at holiday resorts, measure the duration of bright sunshine each day. A widely used simple instrument for this purpose is the Campbell-Stokes sunshine recorder. A clear glass ball about four inches in diameter focuses the Sun's rays on a card mounted in a holder, so positioned that the bright spot where the rays focus moves along the card during the course of the day. The resulting burning chars the card, and provides a visible record of the sunshine. A new card is inserted each day. The card is marked in hours so that the daily sunshine total can be easily measured. Another form of sunshine recorder consists of a blackened glass bulb partly filled with mercury and partly with air. A glass tube dips into the mercury but is sealed off from the air. When the Sun shines, the air in the tube is heated and expands, driving the mercury along the tube to reach two contact points in an electric circuit, and allowing a current to flow. The time for which the current flows is recorded, as sunshine duration.

The importance of measuring the true air temperature was mentioned on page 6, but it should be remembered that this is not necessarily a true measure of the pleasantness or comfort of the weather.

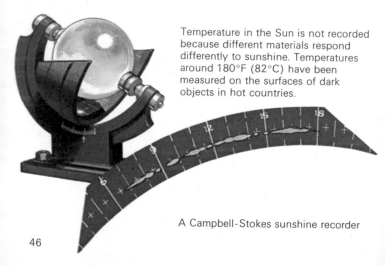

Temperature in the Sun is not recorded because different materials respond differently to sunshine. Temperatures around 180°F (82°C) have been measured on the surfaces of dark objects in hot countries.

A Campbell-Stokes sunshine recorder

Attempts have been made to measure temperature in sunshine with a blackened bulb enclosed in a glass vacuum tube to prevent cooling by the air. This black bulb thermometer is no longer used, however, because identical instruments side by side give different readings.

With a vertical Sun, the amount of energy falling on the Earth's surface is equivalent to a one-bar electric fire per square metre; more than 4,000 per acre.

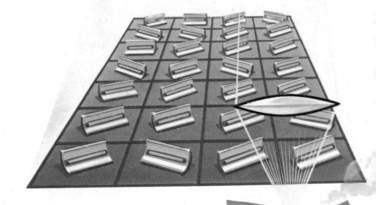

The water-cycle in the earth-atmosphere system

The water-cycle of the Earth and atmosphere

The more common aspects of weather like clouds, rain, snow and fog arise when, because of cooling, the water vapour in the air condenses to liquid, or sometimes to solid, form. Water vapour, although in actual fact it is in amount only a small constituent of the atmosphere, is the most important in regard to weather.

Water vapour gets into the air by evaporation from the oceans, and to a less extent from lakes and rivers. Vegetation in active growth also gives off a large amount of water vapour from its leaves, the supply being drawn from soil moisture, through the roots. This process is called **transpiration**. Water is evaporated into the air mainly from the warmer parts of the oceans and from tropical forests. It is transported upwards, and carried by the winds until it permeates the whole of the troposphere; in particular, the winds carry it into the interiors of the great land masses. It becomes subject to various cooling processes, which will be discussed later, and according to the height and temperature it will form cloud, fog, rain and other types of precipitation.

Most of the water is ultimately returned to the Earth as rain or snow. The rain that falls on the ground may percolate to supply soil moisture to be later returned to the air through transpiration, or to feed springs. It may also remain on the surface giving rise to small streams which combine to form rivers, with or without lakes; this process is called **run-off**. Most of the water in rivers and lakes ultimately finds its way to the sea.

There is, therefore, a continuous process of exchange of water between the land, sea and atmosphere and it is this that is called the **water-cycle**. It has been estimated that if all the water vapour in the atmosphere at any one time were condensed it would supply about ten days' average rainfall for the world as a whole, so we may think of the water-cycle being completed and repeated every ten days or so.

Water vapour is given off from vegetation in a process known as transpiration. It is also evaporated from the world's rivers, lakes and seas. Most of the water returns to the Earth as rain or snow, where it will percolate into the soil or run off the surface as small streams.

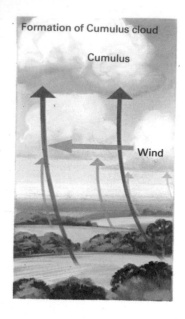

Formation of Cumulus cloud

Cumulus

Wind

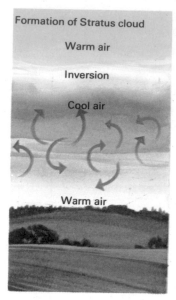

Formation of Stratus cloud

Warm air

Inversion

Cool air

Warm air

Cloud-forming processes

When water in the atmosphere condenses it first becomes visible as a cloud if it is at some upper level, or a fog if it rests on the ground. Cloud consists of minute water droplets, so small that they float in the air and are carried about by the air currents. If the air were absolutely clean and pure the water vapour, on cooling, would not readily condense into visible sizable droplets. But in fact the air is full of minute particles of dust, smoke and salt from sea spray, sometimes thousands of them in a cubic inch, and these stimulate the formation of water droplets around them; they are called **condensation nuclei**.

Clouds have a great variety of forms, from the towering thundercloud to the flat grey pall of a dull winter day. These forms arise from the different processes of cooling by which the vapour is condensed.

The main process of cooling is decompression arising from upward movement of air (page 22). When this movement occurs in an unstable atmosphere the air rises in large bubbles or columns. At a level, dependent on the original temperature and humidity of the rising air, condensation begins; this marks the base of the cloud. The top of the rising column is marked by bulging cauliflower-like heads, which continue to rise until they reach a stable layer. The process is called **convection**, and the type of cloud, from its heaped appearance, is known as Cumulus. There are usually clear spaces between the clouds, and by day the clouds appear brilliantly white from the Sun shining on their tops and sides. Their flat bases and shady sides are usually grey, and between them there is blue sky unless there is a layer of cloud at a higher level.

Vertical motion in the atmosphere is generated also by **turbulence**, the constant stirring of the air due to wind and gustiness. The air goes up and down not in large bubbles but in small filaments or cores, jumbled together. The result is not a few detached clouds but a more or less continuous layer. If there is a stable layer at some upper level the vertical motion is checked, and the air spreads out horizontally, increasing the tendency for the clouds to fuse together into a sheet.

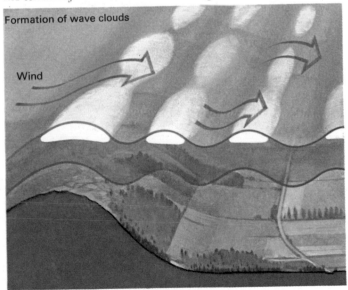

Formation of wave clouds

Wind

A moist layer of air, especially if situated in an inversion of temperature may be cooled by **radiation** and will then give rise to a layer of Stratus cloud. For this reason, Stratus clouds tend to increase by night and diminish by day. Convection clouds, however, which require surface heat for their formation, tend to build up by day, and disappear at night.

When the wind blows across a range of hills, a wave-like motion of air is sometimes set up on the downstream side of the hills. In the crests of the waves air has moved upwards and it may be cooled enough for clouds to form; in the troughs the air warms up and the clouds are evaporated. These clouds tend to remain in the same position relative to the hills and are called **wave clouds**.

Cloud classification

Clouds occur at all heights in the troposphere, but for weather reporting and forecasting it is useful to divide them into three classes, Low, Middle and High clouds.

Low clouds have bases below about 6,500 feet. There are five main types.

Stratus (St) is a grey layer of cloud of uniform height, resembling fog but not resting on the ground. When the layer is broken up, the separate portions are shapeless and featureless. An extensive layer of Stratus sometimes envelopes the upper slopes of hills, which stick up into it. At other times

Stratus (St)

Nimbostratus (NbSt)

Stratus may be formed on the summits and windward slopes of hills, the forced ascent of the wind up the slope leading to cooling and condensation.

Nimbostratus (NbSt) is a low dark grey layer of cloud from which rain or snow usually falls continuously; the rainy cloud of bad weather.

Cumulus (Cu) are thick clouds with vertical development. The base is usually flat, the upper surface dome-shaped with a cauliflower-like structure. The clouds usually occur in detached masses with clear sky between. The bases are usually dark, but the tops and sides may be brightly illuminated by the Sun. A distinction is made between fair weather Cumulus – small clouds of no great vertical extent – and large Cumulus, horizontally extensive and several thousand feet in vertical thickness. Showers of rain and occasionally hail may fall from large Cumulus.

Cumulonimbus (CuNb) is the thundercloud, an extreme development of Cumulus, growing to the level of the tropopause, 30,000 to 50,000 feet, and occasionally higher in the tropics. When seen at a distance these clouds appear like mountains but with the

Cumulus (Cu)

Cumulonimbus (CuNb)

Stratocumulus (StCu)

rounded tops of Cumulus. When overhead they may cover the whole sky and be accompanied by heavy rain, hail, thunder and lightning.

Stratocumulus (StCu), as the name implies, is a layer of cloud composed of a patchwork of flattened Cumulus, soft in outline and grey in colour. It is a very common type.

Middle clouds occur between about 6,500 and 20,000 feet; their middle height range is indicated by the prefix *Alto—*.

Altostratus (ASt) is a uniform grey sheet of cloud. When it is thin and high, the Sun or Moon can be seen through it with a blurred edge, as if through ground glass. Altostratus usually lowers and thickens so that the Sun or Moon can no longer be seen. Very often it changes to Nimbostratus, the rain cloud, but rain may fall from thick Altostratus. Thick Altostratus is of very great vertical depth, often many thousands of feet.

Altocumulus (ACu) is a high form of Stratocumulus. It consists of small, plate-like or flattened, globular masses, which may be light grey near the centres, but white at the edges. They are arranged in groups or lines, sometimes separated by blue sky, sometimes fusing together. *Altocumulus castellanus* is a form of Altocumulus resembling turrets or small towers, sometimes seen before thundery weather.

High clouds are usually thin and white, fibrous or feathery in appearance, from which they are called Cirrus, or take the

Altostratus (ASt)   Altocumulus (ACu)   Altocumulus castellanus

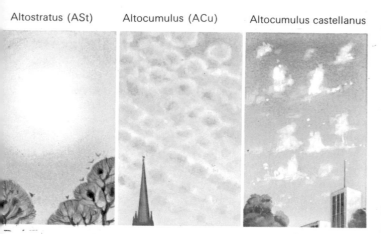

prefix *Cirro*—. They may occur up to heights of 50,000 feet.

Cirrus (Ci) are clouds of a delicate feathery or fibrous appearance, popularly called 'Mares' tails'. They often spread over the whole sky but do not blot out the Sun or Moon; the Sun shines through them strongly enough to cast shadows.

Unlike the low and middle clouds which are composed of liquid water droplets, Cirrus type clouds are composed of ice crystals. They appear in the most varied forms, plumes, tufts and streaks.

Cirrostratus (CiSt) is a thin whitish sheet of cloud which does not blot out the Sun, and gives the sky a milky appearance. It often gives rise to haloes round the Sun or Moon (page 72); frequently it thickens to Altostratus and later to Nimbostratus, and is therefore regarded, with good reason, as a sign of rain.

Cirrocumulus (CiCu) is the most beautiful of all cloud forms – small delicate white cloudlets arranged in lines, groups or ripples, and popularly called 'Mackerel Sky'.

Anvil Cirrus is a special form of plume in the shape of an anvil which is often seen at the top of a thundercloud (Cumulonimbus). It occurs when the water droplets in the Cumulonimbus tops freeze to ice crystals; its peculiar shape is due to the plume of crystals being blown away from the main cloud by strong winds at the higher levels.

Cirrus (Ci)   Cirrostratus (CiSt)   Cirrocumulus (CiCu)

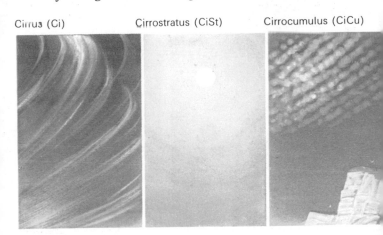

Rainfall

Rain is precipitation in the form of sizable water drops; it falls out of cloud whereas true cloud droplets mostly 'float' in the air. It would seem at first sight that the process of combining cloud droplets to form raindrops is the simple one of amalgamation, but in reality it is complicated, and difficult to simulate in the laboratory. Thousands of cloud droplets are required to make a single raindrop.

Raindrops vary in diameter from about $\frac{1}{2}$ to $5\frac{1}{2}$ millimetres. The latter figure is maximum size; any larger drop, falling through the air breaks up into smaller ones. The resistance of the air sets a maximum speed of fall to each size of drop; small drops fall very slowly, the largest drops at about 8 metres (25 feet) per second. This is comparable with average wind speeds, and explains why, except in very light winds, rain falls slantwise.

There are two main processes by which cloud droplets grow to raindrop size. The first is the water-ice transfer process. If cloud is formed in air at a temperature below freezing many of the droplets do not freeze but remain liquid, in what is called the supercooled state. This can occur down to tem-

(Left) the largest possible raindrop size. $5\frac{1}{2}$ mm. *(Below left)* the smallest raindrop size magnified 60 times with cloud droplets in proportion, and *(right)* condensation nuclei

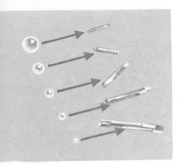

The first process of raindrop formation; the water-ice transfer *(above)* relies on ice particles and supercooled water *(below)*.

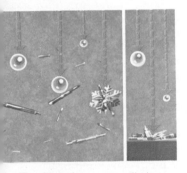

The second process, called coalescence *(below)*; the amalgamation of falling raindrops

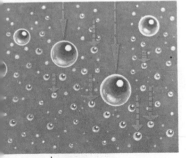

peratures as low as —40° C (—40° F), at which temperature all the droplets freeze. At temperatures just below freezing only a few of the droplets freeze. So a cloud at sub-freezing temperatures consists of a mixture of ice particles and water droplets. The relative humidities of air simultaneously in contact with water and ice are, however, different. For the water it may be just below saturation point and for the ice just above saturation. The water drops will evaporate, but the vapour will condense on the ice particles; the ice particles will thus grow at the expense of the water drops. They fall, arrive in warmer air, and melt into raindrops.

If this water-ice transfer were the only raindrop forming process, all rain would start, in the upper cold levels, as particles of ice. But in the tropics rain often falls from clouds which could not possibly contain ice because their temperature is not low enough. There is then, another rain forming process; this is called coalescence. A few large drops, falling through the slower falling small drops, collide with them and, so to speak, capture them, to form still larger drops.

Measurement of rainfall

The amount of rain which falls in a specified time is expressed as the depth of water it would produce on a large, level impermeable surface. It is usually expressed in millimetres, although many observers in English-speaking countries use inches and hundredths. As little as 5 mm of rain falling continuously over several hours are enough to produce an unpleasantly rainy day. A day with 1 inch (25 mm) spread over several hours is thoroughly wet. One inch of rain is equivalent to 101 tons of water per acre of ground.

Rainfall is measured daily at a very large number of stations. The simple **raingauge** consists of a copper or plastic funnel, so mounted that the catch of rain is collected in a bottle or other vessel which is itself protected from the rain. The water collected in the bottle is poured into the rain measure – a glass vessel with graduations so designed, in relation to its own diameter and that of the funnel, that the amount of rainfall can be read directly.

In measuring rainfall with the standard type of gauge, certain precautions have to be taken. If the rim of the funnel is too near the ground, splashing of rain into the gauge makes it read too high. On the other hand, winds blowing over the funnel set up eddies, which cause the gauge to catch too little rain, so that it should be placed as low as possible. One foot above the ground is a good compromise. The gauge should be in an open situation not sheltered by trees or buildings.

Types of rain

Air can be cooled in various ways in the atmosphere, for example, by radiation, by contact with a cold surface, and by

Raingauges are usually read daily, but in remote areas they may be visited only once a month; then specially designed gauges to hold a month's rainfall must be used. Many official stations have recording raingauges *(right)*. In one type, the rain accumulating in the container below the funnel operates a float which moves a pen to trace a record on the usual strip chart. In another, the rain from the funnel is led into a small vessel which empties automatically at intervals of 10 mm of rain, at the same time registering this amount of rain on the record *(right)*.

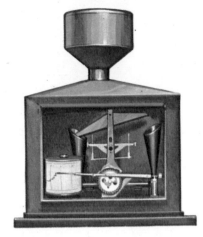

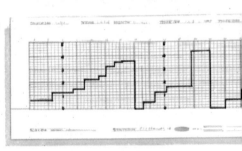

The ordinary raingauge *(left)* and the recording raingauge are not very suitable for indicating the rate of rainfall over periods of a few minutes, because the amount of water they collect is too small to be measured accurately. A few stations have gauges for this special purpose, which have very large funnels about three feet in diameter, so that the water they collect over short periods can be easily measured.

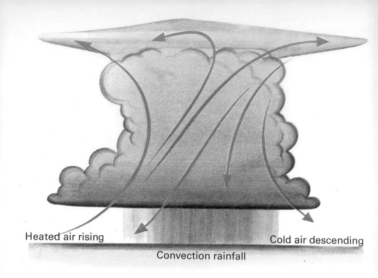

Heated air rising

Cold air descending

Convection rainfall

expansion on rising (page 22). Of these, only the last is effective in producing rain. Rising air currents may however be brought about in different ways and thereby produce different types of rain.

When convection cloud (page 24) penetrates to higher and higher levels, more and more water vapour is condensed and the heavier is the resulting rainfall. Convection clouds (large Cu and CuNb) are rarely more than a few miles across and between them there is often clear sky. **Convection rain** therefore, consists of showers which are of limited extent, and, since there is usually some wind, the showers do not, as a rule, last long at any one place. Hence the expression 'showers and bright intervals', which often occurs in weather forecasts. If the convection is extremely vigorous the shower develops into a thunderstorm (page 66). Most of the rainfall of the tropics is of the convective type because of the strong heating of the ground. For the same reason, in temperate latitudes over land, showers are most likely to occur on warm afternoons. Showers are frequent also in cold air flowing over a warm sea surface: The up-currents of air in convection cloud retard the fall of the raindrops allowing them time to grow to larger sizes; convection rain is therefore fairly heavy as a rule.

Cyclonic rain is due to a general rise of air over a large area, perhaps three hundred miles wide and several hundreds of miles long. It is associated with depressions and their accompanying fronts (pages 84 to 87). The rain falls steadily, sometimes for many hours, from an extensive cover of NbSt or thick ASt of great depth. The forced rise of damp winds when they meet a mountain range or high coastline causes **orographic rain**. The windward slopes become blanketed with cloud from which rain or drizzle falls. On the leeward side the air is descending and warming, the cloud tends to break up and the rain eases or stops altogether; such an area is called a **rain shadow**.

Most of the Earth's rainfall is not simply one or other of these types but a combination of them. Near the western coasts of Europe and North America the cyclonic and orographic factors often give heavy falls on the western mountain slopes, but only light rain in the shadow areas to the east.

Cyclonic rain is associated with the passage of fronts in a depression *(below)* and occurs at any time of the day or night. In temperate or high latitudes it may occur at any season.

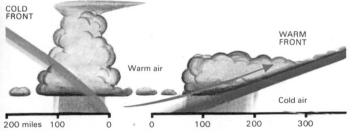

Areas of orographic rainfall *(below)* include the coastal regions of the United States and Canada, western Norway and the western parts of the British Isles. There are corresponding rain shadows to eastwards of these regions.

Extreme falls of rain

The heaviest rates of rainfall, such as occur in so-called cloudbursts, are only maintained for periods of a few minutes. It is not to be expected that the heaviest rainfall in one hour will be twelve times that recorded in five minutes. The shorter the period over which it is measured, the higher is the extreme recorded rate of rainfall. Some published figures are:

Highest rainfall	Amount	Place	Date
1 year	905 inches	Cherrapunji, India	1861
1 month	366 inches	Cherrapunji, India	1861
1 day	73·6 inches	Reunion Island	March, 1952
1 hour	12·0 inches	Missouri, USA	June, 1907
15 minutes	7·8 inches	Jamaica	May, 1916
5 minutes	2·5 inches	Panama	November, 1911
1 minute	1·23 inches	Maryland, USA	July, 1956

Scarcely a year passes without flood disasters in some part of the world. **Floods** may be merely local, as when a summer thunderstorm produces a deluge too heavy for the drainage system in a built-up area. The more serious floods occur when

heavy rain falls over a river catchment area; the main area affected is often far away downstream, particularly in riverside towns.

A long period without appreciable rain is a **drought**. In Great Britain a 'Partial Drought' is said to occur when, over 29 consecutive days the average daily rainfall does not exceed 0·01 inches; an 'Absolute Drought' is a period of 15 days each having less than 0·01 inches. In the developed countries droughts do not usually have serious consequences, but a succession of months with rainfall well below average leads to water shortage, as in New York in 1965. In tropical countries, for example North Australia, East Africa and India, failure of the rains, which normally only occur at certain seasons, leads to loss of livestock, crop failure and famine.

Drizzle is very small drops of rain, larger than cloud droplets, and big enough to fall rather than float. It may be orographic or cyclonic in origin, but not convectional since it falls from cloud with no great vertical development.

Heavy rain will sometimes transform an area of drought *(left)* into one of flood *(below)*.

Snow

Precipitation in the form of ice crystals which agglomerate forms flakes of **snow**. Obviously in the cloud levels where the snow originates the temperature must be below freezing. If the temperature is high enough between the cloud level and the ground the snow will melt as it falls and turn to rain. At temperatures only a little above freezing partial melting takes place. Snow can occur at ground level with temperatures up to about 4° C (39° F). At these higher temperatures the snow consists of large flakes because the partial melting allows the smaller flakes to stick together. If the temperature is well below freezing the snowflakes are small, dry and powdery. Powdery snow, when it settles on the ground, is not slippery. The reason why snow is such a nuisance to traffic in the milder parts of Europe and the United States is that it is very near the melting point and easily compacted by traffic to form slippery ice. Very cold snow will not bind into a snowball, neither does it compact on the roads. For this reason, traffic in the colder parts of Canada and eastern Europe is not badly affected by the persistent winter snow cover.

In water content, about 10 inches of newly fallen snow are equivalent to one inch of rain. The depth of snow can be

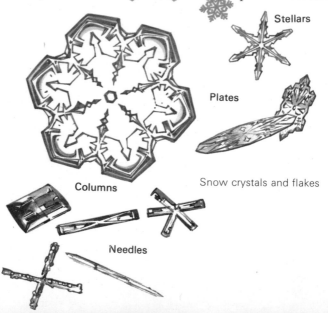

Stellars

Plates

Columns

Snow crystals and flakes

Needles

measured on a graduated pole placed vertically in an open situation. To use these readings for estimating equivalent rainfall the observation should be made daily, or at even shorter intervals, because over a period the snow layer contracts by melting, or compression under its own weight. If a raingauge is used it must either be heated to melt the snow as it falls, or the snow must be melted by the observer when he reads the gauge. Snowfalls heavy enough to bury a gauge are difficult to measure accurately.

Drifting snow is a hazard in windy weather. The snow tends to remain airborne where the winds are strongest and it is swept up from the ground in the more exposed places. It is deposited where the winds are lighter – in gullies and depressions. Obstacles like buildings and hedges create wind eddies – a patchwork of gusts and lulls – again causing drifting into places where the winds are lighter, and the worst drifts may occur on the sheltered side of a building.

Sleet is a name given to two different phenomena. In the British Isles it is a mixture of rain and snow, but in the United States it is frozen rain, that is pellets of ice. The rain-snow mixture occurs when the temperature is too high for pure snow and too low for pure rain.

The equivalent of 1 in of rain is 10 ins of newly fallen snow

Thunderstorms

A thunderstorm is rain or hail accompanied by thunder and lightning. The main condition for its occurrence is great atmospheric instability, giving rise to rapid convection to great heights of a mass of very moist air. It is marked by a towering anvil-shaped Cumulonimbus cloud, with a dark turbulent base; the cloud rises to 30,000 feet or more.

The thunder and **lightning** arise from electrical charges. In the turbulent conditions inside the cloud the raindrops are broken up; the smaller droplets are carried to the top of the cloud, the larger ones remaining at lower levels. Or the drops may freeze, throwing off small ice spicules which are carried to the top of the cloud. These processes of separation lead to the separation of electric charges. When the insulation of the air breaks down a lightning stroke results, sometimes entirely within the cloud, but sometimes from cloud to earth. The lightning travels along thin channels, usually branched, hence the name forked-lightning. At a distance it is often obscured by clouds, and only seen as a flash of diffuse light, called sheet-lightning.

On passing through the air the lightning momentarily gives rise to great heat. The resulting sudden expansion and contraction of the air sets up sound waves, which are heard as **thunder**. The sound from the different parts of the lightning is not all heard at the same time and this, with echoes, gives the reverberation characteristic of thunder. Sound travels a mile in about five seconds, so the time in seconds between hearing the thunder and seeing the lightning divided by five, results in the approximate distance of the lightning, in miles.

Lightning is attracted to sharp points which stick up towards the cloud. Tall buildings, therefore, are protected by lightning conductors, spiked rods connected to broad bands of metal which lead the lightning discharge safely to earth. Isolated tall trees also attract lightning, and it is risky to shelter under them during a thunderstorm. Spaces enclosed by metal, like cars and aeroplanes give complete protection.

Thunderstorms up to about 1,000 miles distant are located by a device known as **sferic**. This enables two stations observing a flash simultaneously, to locate the flash at the point of intersection of direction lines drawn from each station.

The top of a thundercloud accumulates positive charges, the bottom negative. Electric pressures of millions of volts are then built up *(right)*.

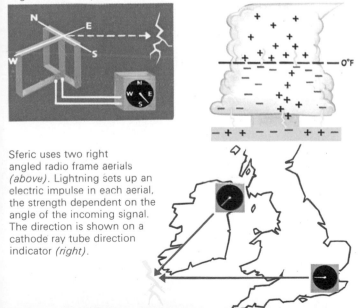

Sferic uses two right angled radio frame aerials *(above)*. Lightning sets up an electric impulse in each aerial, the strength dependent on the angle of the incoming signal. The direction is shown on a cathode ray tube direction indicator *(right)*.

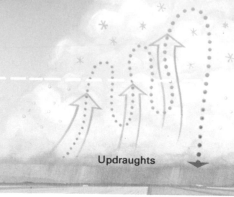

Formation of hailstones

Mainly ice crystals

32°F

Mainly water droplets

Updraughts

The hailstone formation processes may be repeated many times. The frozen water is clear ice, the gathered crystals white, so that a fully developed hailstone, if cut in half, is found to consist of alternate layers of clear and opaque ice.

Hail is precipitation in the form of pellets or lumps of ice, usually occurring in thunderstorms. A large raindrop near the bottom of a thundercloud in a strong up-current will be carried upwards and, reaching lower temperatures will freeze to ice. It then gathers ice crystals and snowflakes in the upper part of the cloud and, getting larger, begins to fall. In the lower part of the cloud it collects more water. It may once again be caught in an up-current and be carried towards the top of the cloud, freezing again and collecting more ice crystals.

Most hailstones are a quarter of an inch or less in diameter, but some grow much bigger and do much damage, especially to fragile structures like glasshouses. Even the smaller stones cause serious damage to crops and are a regular hazard in southern Europe and parts of the United States. Aircraft flying through hailstorms are subject to short but intense bombardment, which leaves the aircraft alarmingly pitted. Fortunately, with radar, pilots can usually take avoiding action.

Black ice is extremely dangerous to road traffic and will also build up on other objects. Ice and frost often affect aircraft and telephone and power lines may break under the strain with disruption to communications and power supplies.

Ice and frost

Occasionally rain falls from a layer of warm air a few hundred feet up through an air layer near the ground whose temperature is below freezing. The drops freeze on passing through the cold air and reach the ground as small ice crystals or white pellets which are called **soft hail**. A much more serious hazard arises when the drops become supercooled (page 57). Then they freeze immediately on coming into contact with the surface, covering roads with a film of 'Black Ice'. This is extremely dangerous because it is not easily seen. Similarly telephone wires and tree branches become coated heavily with layers of ice, the weight of which often breaks them down.

At night, under a clear sky, the ground cools to below air temperature (page 9). Moisture in the air near the ground condenses, and is deposited as dew. If there is a ground frost the deposit is in the form of white ice particles, called **hoar frost** or 'White Frost'.

Visibility, fog and mist

Visibility is the greatest distance at which objects may be recognized, not merely seen as a faint blur. At weather observing stations a number of objects at known distances are selected and the visibility recorded as the distance of the farthest of them recognizable.

Fog is said to occur when the visibility is below 1,000 metres. This is the seeing distance below which aircraft begin to experience difficulty in landing. In everyday life, however, in particular for road traffic, fog is a visibility of 200 yards or less. Conditions with visibility somewhat above the fog limit are called mist, or haze. Mist is caused by water droplets, haze by dust or smoke.

Fog is really cloud resting on the ground, and is caused by cooling and condensation in moist air. **Radiation fog** occurs on calm clear sky nights, mainly in autumn and winter. The ground cools rapidly, cools the air in contact with it, and the condensed moisture appears as fog, which deepens as the cooling continues. The thickest fogs occur in mild damp air because of the large amount of water vapour available for condensation. Radiation fog tends to accumulate in valleys and

To record visibility, objects at known distances are chosen. For the farthest distance *(above)*, features of the terrain like hills or woods are

chosen; for the middle distance, buildings and trees and for the nearest distance *(below)* small objects such as posts and shrubs.

Radiation fog

Sea mist

Hill fog

Freezing fog

over low-lying ground, because cold air, being heavy, tends to collect there. It is worse in the country or parks than in built-up areas, for the heating of the buildings keeps cities warmer.

When a current of mild damp air flows over a cold surface, **advection fog** occurs. It is especially a feature of sea areas and the adjacent coasts in spring and early summer, when the water is cold and can occur under cloudy skies and with moderate or strong winds. A form of advection fog is **hill fog** which occurs when a current of damp air is forced to rise on meeting elevated ground. It envelops the windward slopes and summits, whereas with radiation fog the higher ground is often clear.

Estimation of visibility by reference to objects at known distances cannot generally be used at night. At important airfields more sophisticated methods are essential. One such method is to measure and record electronically the strength of the light incident on a receiver from a lamp of standard brightness at a fixed distance. This gives a measure of the transparency of the air – effectively the visibility.

Freezing fog is fog with air temperature below freezing. It leads to ice deposit on car windscreens, a common hazard. The droplets are often supercooled (page 57) and freeze immediately on contact with trees, power lines and other objects, leading to accumulating deposits of ice, known as **rime**.

Optical phenomena

A **rainbow** is a circular arc of coloured light which displays the colours of the visible spectrum, violet on the inside and red on the outside. The centre of the circle is the point opposite to the Sun (in the sky considered as a sphere surrounding the Earth). The centre therefore is never above the horizon and the rainbow never greater than a half circle; the higher the Sun in the sky the smaller the rainbow. The light from the Sun is reflected and refracted inside raindrops in such a way that it is split up into the spectrum colours and emerges at an angle of $42°$ to the direction of the Sun's rays. The observer therefore sees a circular arc of $42°$ radius. Obviously the Sun must be shining and rain falling at the same time, so that rainbows are seen in showery weather. Additional reflections sometimes produce a secondary bow fainter than the main one, and outside it, with the colours in reverse order. Occasionally a rainbow is seen by moonlight, it is very faint and the colours cannot be distinguished. When a veil of Cirrostratus cloud (page 54) covers the sky, various rings of whitish light are seen round the Sun or Moon; these are called haloes. They are caused by the refraction of light by the ice crystals of which

Halo and Mock Sun

Corona

the cloud is composed. The most common halo is one at an angular radius of 22° from the Sun or Moon.

If the cloud is not a continuous sheet, a partial halo may be seen, in particular bright spots at 22° angular distance on one or both sides of the sun; they are sometimes faintly coloured and are called **mock suns**. A **corona** is a set of coloured rings closely surrounding the Sun or Moon. It is caused by refraction of light rays by water droplets which form a thin layer of cloud, usually Altocumulus. The presence of a corona is evidence that the cloud particles are water and not ice. Faint patches of colour resembling mother of pearl are sometimes seen in water drop cloud at some distance from the Sun, a phenomenon called **iridescence**.

On hot days the air near the ground becomes more strongly heated than that higher up, so that rays of light passing near the ground are bent upwards. The result is that an observer looking at the ground 100 yards or so away from him sees light from the sky giving the impression of a pool of water on the ground. This is known as a **mirage** and is common on roads on summer days, and in deserts where thirsty travellers have been deluded into thinking that water is there.

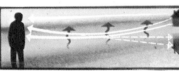

Diagrammatic representation *(above)* of the bending of light rays to produce the mirage effect of hot days *(left)*

Rainbow

73

WEATHER MAPS AND FORECASTING
Collection and distribution of observations

As a starting point the weather forecaster requires to know the existing state of the weather over a large area around him. The size of this area depends upon the duration of the period for which he is forecasting; for the usual twenty-four hour forecast in Britain the area extends from the western North Atlantic to Central Europe and from the Mediterranean to Iceland and northern Scandinavia. A correspondingly large area, extending well out into the Pacific, is required by forecasters in the United States and Canada. To meet this need, observations are made at regular intervals at a network of stations covering the area, and provision must be made for communicating them promptly to the forecasting centre. Weather forecasting was not possible at all before the invention of the telegraph about the middle of the last century, and information from the oceans, from observations made by ships, was not available until the invention of wireless telegraphy, early in the present century. There is a complex world-wide system of meteorological communications sponsored by the World Meteorological Organization with headquarters in Geneva, Switzerland, and of which nearly all

Diagrammatic representation of data exchange

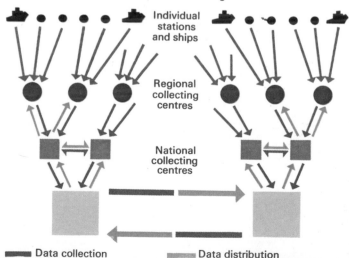

Individual stations and ships

Regional collecting centres

National collecting centres

Data collection   Data distribution

nations (with the notable exception of China) are members.

Stations observe and report at four principal hours of the day, 00, 06, 12 and 18 hours GMT, now called Universal Time (UT). Stations immediately transmit their reports to collecting centres in their own country (or region). The centres combine the reports into single collective messages, which are transmitted according to fixed time schedules, for reception by forecasting centres throughout the world.

It would obviously be impracticable to exchange all this information in plain language – the messages would be far too long. So a figure code has been agreed internationally. A report from a station consists of a set of groups each of five figures, for example:—

01437   82612   26235   10714   . . .

The first group is a number which identifies the reporting station. The meanings of the other figures depend on their position in the message. For example the last two figures in group 2 give the wind speed (12 knots); the last two figures in group 4 the temperature ($14°$ C, ($57°$ F)).

For ships the code is somewhat modified; for example latitude and longitude are required instead of a station identifier and upper air observations also need special codes. There are in fact a large number of codes to meet special requirements.

Symbols		Cloud types		Cloud cover (in eighths of the sky)	
●	Rain		Cirrus	◯	0
●●	Continuous slight rain		Cirrocumulus	◉	1
●●●	Continuous heavy rain		Cirrostratus		
			Nimbostratus	◔	2
✳	Snow		Stratocumulus	◔	3
✱	Sleet		Cumulus	◑	4
↳	Thunderstorm		Altocumulus	◖	5
▽	Shower		Altostratus	◕	6
△	Hail		Stratus	◕	7
≡	Fog		Cumulonimbus		

Synoptic charts

The communications system provides the forecaster with a large mass of figures; the next step is to put them into a form suitable for study. This is done by plotting the observations on a large outline map which in popular terms is called a Weather Map, technically a Synoptic Chart. Simplified synoptic charts appear in some newspapers and are shown in connection with the weather forecasts on television.

On the forecasters' synoptic chart the position of each station is marked by a small circle. The report for each station is plotted in and around the circle. Some elements like temperature and pressure are entered in plain figures. Others like rain, snow, fog and cloud, not easily expressed in figures are plotted in internationally agreed symbols. This has the advantage that pilots can readily interpret synoptic charts at meteorological offices at airports in any part of the world.

Some of the symbols used are shown on this page as well as an example of a complete plot for a station. The meanings to be attached to the figures and symbols depend upon where they are placed in relation to the station circle. Thus the amount of shading in the circle indicates the proportion of sky covered by cloud, the temperature (in whole degrees) is written to the upper left of the circle, the sea-level pressure in millibars and tenths to the upper right. (The hundreds figure for the pressure, that is the initial 9 or 10 is omitted as being understood since the pressure is almost always between 950 and 1050 millibars. Thus 987 = 998·7 mb, 125 = 1012·5 mb). The wind is represented by an arrow flying with the wind and drawn towards the station circle: the speed by 'feathers' on the wind arrow, a short feather indicating 5 knots, a large one 10 knots, a long and a short 15 knots and so on.

At forecasting centres the plotting is carried out as the reports are received, by an assistant sitting beside the forecaster. Charts covering small areas like the British Isles can be completely plotted within half an hour of the observations being made, those for large areas such as North America and the Atlantic and Europe, in two to three hours. A modern development is the automatic plotter, which is fed by the data on punched paper tape, and plots the chart with all the station data in their correct locations.

Reports from each weather station are plotted in and around a circle, which denotes the position of the station, as illustrated in the model *(right)*. *(Below)* an enlarged section of a synoptic chart

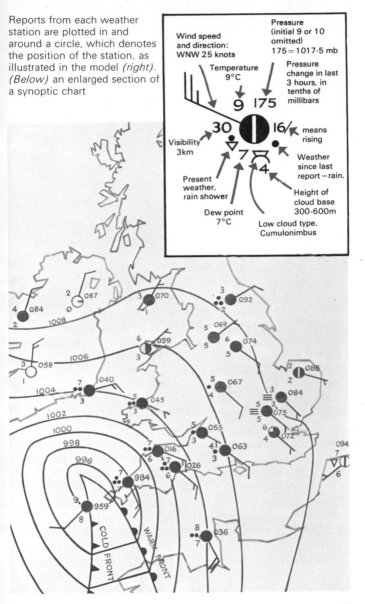

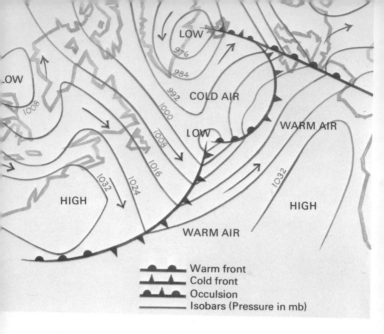

	Warm front
	Cold front
	Occulsion
	Isobars (Pressure in mb)

When the plotting of the synoptic chart is completed the forecaster then proceeds to the analysis, the object of which is to systematize the collection of individual station plots into a coherent picture. The first step is to draw the isobars – lines along which the pressure is the same. They are of the same nature as contours, which are lines of equal altitude on a geographical map. Just as contour lines are drawn at intervals of 50, 100 or 1,000 feet according to the scale of the map, so isobars may be drawn at intervals of 1, 2 or 4 millibars.

The pressure values plotted on a weather map are adjusted to sea level (page 12). The reason is that, if station level pressures were used, two stations only a mile or two apart and differing in height by 1,000 feet would show a pressure difference of about 30 millibars. If the stations were at the same level the pressure difference would be most unlikely to exceed half a millibar. Thus height differences completely mask the true horizontal pressure differences, and a map of station level pressures would be to all intents and purposes a contour map and no help to the forecaster.

The cartographer in drawing contours is guided only by the

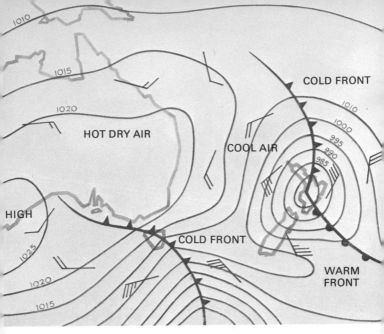

Typical synoptic charts for northern *(left)* and southern hemispheres

plotted heights. The meteorologist in drawing isobars has an additional aid in the plotted wind observations. The winds blow nearly parallel to the isobars, crossing them at a small angle towards the lower pressure; in the northern hemisphere the lower pressure is to the left of the wind, in the southern hemisphere to the right, and the stronger the wind the closer are the isobars.

The completed isobars usually reveal a few standard patterns. A set of curved isobars surrounding low pressure is called a depression; if surrounding high pressure it is called an anticyclone, corresponding to a mountain peak on a geographical contour map.

Open V-shaped isobars with low pressure inside (corresponding to a valley) delineate a trough of low pressure; if the high pressure is inside (corresponding to a spur or ridge) the formation is called a ridge of high pressure. As will be seen in later pages, these isobar formations are important because they fix the general character of the weather in their areas.

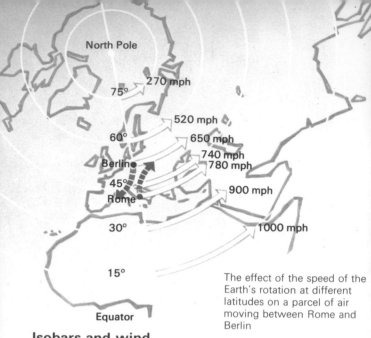

North Pole

75° 270 mph

520 mph

60° 650 mph

740 mph

780 mph

Berlin

45°

Rome 900 mph

30° 1000 mph

15°

Equator

The effect of the speed of the Earth's rotation at different latitudes on a parcel of air moving between Rome and Berlin

Isobars and wind

The statement on page 79 that the winds blow nearly parallel to the isobars is puzzling because it seems natural to think that the air should move directly from high to low pressure, that is cross the isobars at right angles. This apparently odd behaviour arises from the rotation of the Earth. The above simple illustration shows that direct flow from high to low pressure will not in fact occur. Suppose that the isobars over Europe run from west to east with low pressure to the north. A parcel of air over Rome, for example, would begin to move northwards and, continuing, would in time arrive over Berlin which is due north of Rome. Berlin being in latitude 52° N is nearer the Earth's axis than Rome (lattitude 42° N) and, there-fore, because of the Earth's rotation, is moving eastwards more slowly than Rome. The eastward speeds are Rome 780 mph, Berlin 650 mph. The air moving northward from Rome would retain the eastward speed of 780 mph and therefore on arrival in the latitude of Berlin would have an excess eastward speed of 780 minus 650, that is 130 mph. It would in fact have become a west wind, with the lower pressure to the north, or on the left. Similarly, if the higher pressure lay to the north, a northerly wind starting from Berlin would become easterly on reaching the latitude of Rome – again with low pressure to its left. The same argument applied to the southern hemisphere shows that north and south winds are deviated so as to blow with low pressure to their right.

The foregoing simple argument is not complete, but it can be shown mathematically that the rule applies to all directions of winds and isobars. The law of Buys Ballot, a famous Dutch meteorologist of the 19th century states that:

(i) The winds blow nearly parallel to the isobars crossing them at a small angle from high to low pressure.

(ii) If you stand with your back to the wind the lower pressure will be to your left in the northern, to your right in the southern hemisphere.

(iii) The closer the isobars the stronger the wind.

It is easy to see that, in the northern hemisphere, the winds will blow anticlockwise round a depression and clockwise round an anticyclone; vice versa in the southern hemisphere.

Speed of eastward movement of the Earth's surface in various latitudes, due to daily rotation. Variation of speed causes air currents to swing right in the northern, left in the southern hemisphere.

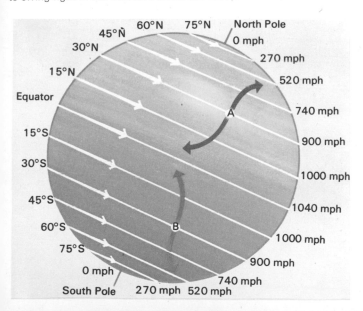

Air masses

The qualities, vaguely described as the feel of the air, are usually similar over a very large area, and the whole extent of the air with these nearly uniform properties is called an air mass. An air mass acquires its qualities by stagnating for some days, for example over a hot desert, a tropical ocean or the polar regions. These are called source regions. When it leaves the source it carries its qualities with it to the regions to which it moves, although they may be modified during transit.

According to the latitude of the source region, an air mass is described as equatorial, tropical, Arctic or polar. The term polar should be strictly sub-polar since it applies to the high latitude belt outside the Arctic. There is a further categorization according to whether the air starts over an ocean or land area (the latter including an ice-covered ocean); they are designated maritime and continental respectively.

Over Europe the principal air masses are Arctic (A), maritime polar (mP), continental polar (cP), maritime tropical (mT) and continental tropical (cT). Arctic air is cold in summer, very cold in winter. If it reaches western Europe from the north it has a long track over a relatively warm sea, and becomes unstable (page 22). Frequent showers develop in it, in winter of snow. If it follows a track over Russia it is dry, and in winter, bitterly cold.

Continental polar air in winter is similar to Arctic air. In summer it is dry and fairly warm because even the north of the continent has high summer temperatures. Maritime polar

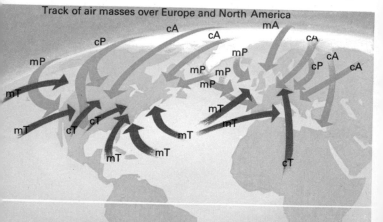

Track of air masses over Europe and North America

air is cool and showery; clear, crisp and invigorating. Even in winter it is comparatively mild because the North Atlantic is warm. Maritime tropical air is mild in winter. In summer it is cloudy and rather cool but humid and often foggy on the coasts; well inland the clouds break up and the weather becomes warm. Continental tropical air reaches Europe from the Sahara; it is very dry and in summer gives rise to heat waves. In winter it gives pleasant mild weather.

Over North America the principal air masses are designated similarly to those for Europe. West of the Rockies they have similar properties to the European air masses. North America, unlike Europe, however, has the great barrier of the Rockies running from north to south, so that Pacific air masses do not easily penetrate into the continent. Instead the way is open for A and cP air to sweep southwards, bringing bitterly cold weather, sometimes as far south as Florida. Off the north-eastern seaboard the Atlantic is cold and mP air masses are colder than in Europe. Maritime tropical air from the Gulf of Mexico is warm and moist and may give rise to heavy rain.

The Australasian area is an example of southern hemisphere air masses. On the north coast of Australia, maritime air is tropical or equatorial in origin, hot and humid. Both mT and mP air affect the eastern and western coastal regions, only mP the south coast. The interior acts as a source region for cT air which is very hot and dry in summer, warm and dry in winter. The two main masses of New Zealand are oceanic in origin, mT and mP, and have similar properties to those of Europe.

Track of air masses over Australia and New Zealand

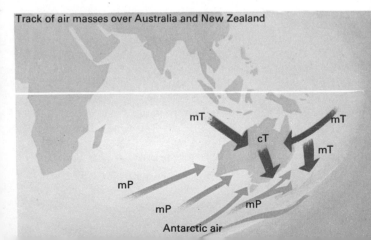

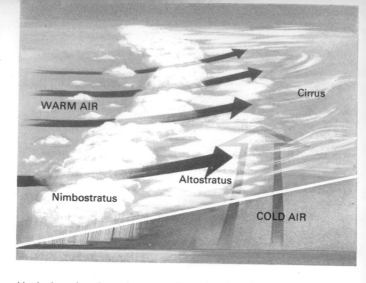

Vertical section through a warm front showing air movement, clouds and precipitation

Fronts

Fronts are the boundary regions between different air masses, usually warm and cold masses. Throughout an air mass conditions are more or less uniform but sharp changes occur in comparatively narrow regions at the fronts. These changes give rise to thick cloud and rain and this is why fronts are such important features in weather study.

The most significant fronts are those having warm damp air on one side and cold, usually dry, air on the other. The warm air being light tends to rise above the heavier cold air. Alternatively, the heavy cold air may be thought of as cutting under the lighter warm air. In either case the surface separating the two air masses will be not vertical but sloping, with the warm air uppermost, the cold air lying underneath it in the form of a wedge. The slope is roughly 1 in 100. Fronts are usually several hundreds of miles long and extend vertically to the upper part of the troposphere. As a rule they move more or less steadily sideways, although occasionally they are stationary. If the cold air is retreating, so that as the front passes over a place the temperature there goes up, the front is called a warm front. If the cold air is advancing the temperature change is reversed and the front is called a cold front.

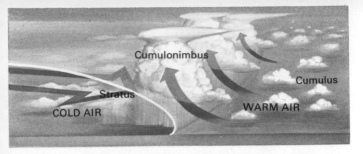

Vertical section through a cold front *(compare picture on left)*

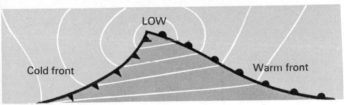

Isobars and fronts in model depression (northern hemisphere)

A cold front is usually more steeply sloped than a warm front.

At a warm front, the warm air is rising along and above the sloping surface, and is therefore subject to cooling and condensation. Some 500 miles ahead of the front at the surface, where the sloping surface is about 5 miles high, only thin Cirrus cloud is formed but as the frontal surface lowers the cloud gradually thickens to produce the sequence Cirrostratus, Altostratus and Nimbostratus, with rain. The rain belt ahead of a warm front is often 200 to 300 miles wide. The heaviest rain occurs near where the front passes at ground level. The temperature then begins to rise, the rain eases and the cloud thins and may even break up.

A cold front produces a similar sequence in reverse but the changes are more rapid and violent because of the greater slope. A short period of heavy rain occurs at the frontal passage, the clouds are often Cumulonimbus, dark and threatening. The sequence Altostratus, Cirrostratus, Cirrus occurs in a narrow belt behind the front and the sky often clears quickly. But the cold air is usually unstable so that Cumulus and Cumulonimbus clouds with showers develop readily, giving rise to characteristic cool showery weather.

Frontal structure of depressions

A depression, as its name implies, is a region of low barometric pressure and appears on the synoptic chart as a set of closed curved isobars with winds circulating anticlockwise in the northern hemisphere, clockwise in the southern. Its weather is characteristically unsettled, usually wet and stormy, but there may be limited intervals of fair weather. Depressions vary widely in size; their diameters may be anything between about 200 and 2,000 miles and it is not unusual for a depression centred over Iceland to extend over the whole of Scandinavia and the British Isles. Depressions move and carry their bad weather with them; the most usual movement is from a direction between southwest and northwest; movement from the east is rare. To say that a depression moves does not connote material movement; it is a disturbance propagated through the air as an ocean wave is a disturbance and not an identifiable body of water. When the pressure at the centre is very low, that is when many isobars enclose it a depression is said to be deep; a shallow depression is one with only a few closed isobars.

In the early stages of its development a depression has both a warm and a cold front which form a continuous line running through the centre. The warm front lies in a curve towards the southeast; the cold front towards the southwest. Cold air lies in the wide sector to north of the front, warm air in the narrow sector to the south; this is called the Warm

Vertical section through warm and cold fronts near the centre of a depression where the fronts are close together

Sector. A wide belt of cloud and rain lies to north and northeast of the warm front, and along the cold front is a narrower belt of cloud and heavier rain. Within the warm sector the weather is mild and damp, often with drizzle, low cloud and hill fog. As well as the cloud and rain and temperature changes at fronts, there are also changes of pressure and wind. As a warm front approaches, the barometer falls slowly at first more steeply near the front. At the same time, the wind backs to south or southeast (in the northern hemisphere; in the southern hemisphere it veers to north or northeast), and increases in strength. As the front passes, the pressure fall is arrested and the wind veers to southwest (northwest in the southern hemisphere). At the cold front the pressure begins to rise and the wind veers to west, northwest or even north (west, southwest or south in the southern hemisphere). These changes are more or less abrupt, especially at the cold front. The isobars bend sharply at the fronts, a formation which is called a **trough of low pressure**, the lower pressure being on the inside of the V-shaped bend.

Development of a depression:

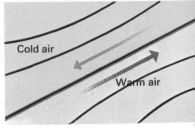

(1) Front with opposing air currents

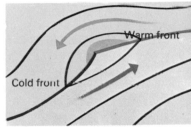

(2) A wave develops in the front

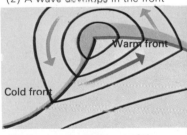

(3) Further development of the wave

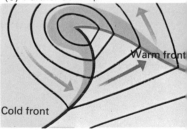

(4) Fully developed depression

87

On the synoptic chart the first sign of an incipient depression is a local weakening of the wind and a widening out of the isobars somewhere along a trailing cold front. A wave-shaped distortion appears on the front, and a small low pressure centre develops at the crest of the wave. In the immediately surrounding area the pressure begins to fall. A disturbance of this kind is called a **wave depression**. Since at this stage it is a minor feature on the frontal system of a distant larger depression, it is also called a **secondary depression**. The new feature develops rapidly and moves quickly along the front; the wave on the front grows in size and the number of isobars surrounding it increases as the new system acquires a wind circulation of its own. The forward (eastward) part of the wave, with advancing warm air, is now a warm front; the rear (westward) part, of course, continues as a cold front.

The fully developed system now has warm and cold fronts meeting at the centre. Between these is a mass of warm air which is climbing up the warm front surface and being undercut by cold air at the cold front. The two fronts coalesce and the resulting single front, a combination of the former warm and cold fronts, is called an **occlusion**. The process of occlusion takes place first at the centre of the depression and gradually works outwards so that, at some distance from the centre, there remains a warm sector. At an occlusion there is still warm air at some upper level, bounded by two sloping frontal surfaces, so that the weather experienced as an occlusion approaches and passes is a combination of warm and cold front weather – lowering and thickening cloud, rain, a rapid clearance followed by showers.

During the occluding process a new centre sometimes forms at the point of occlusion (where the warm and cold fronts separate); such a centre often develops rapidly and may become the main system. The occlusion is caught up in the developing circulation and, being to north of the new centre, it will move westwards at first, later swinging southwards and eastwards and is effectively a third front; it usually has cold front characteristics.

Development of a new depression from a wave-like disturbance at the cold front of an existing depression

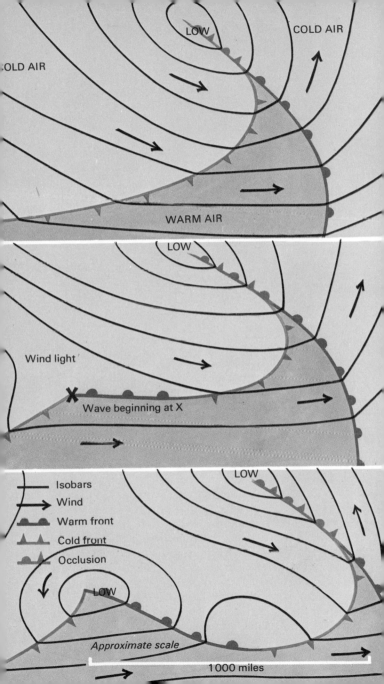

LOW

COLD AIR

COLD AIR

WARM AIR

LOW

Wind light

X

Wave beginning at X

LOW

— Isobars

→ Wind

Warm front

Cold front

Occlusion

LOW

LOW

Approximate scale

1 000 miles

An anticyclone *(left)* appears on the synoptic chart as a set of closed isobars with the highest pressure at the centre. In this and other respects it is the opposite of the depression; the winds circulate clockwise in the northern hemisphere, anticlockwise in the southern.

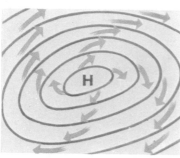

Section through an anticyclone showing air flow *(above right)* and the typical weather of summer and winter *(right)*. Anticyclonic weather is dry and settled but, in winter, it may be persistently dull if cloud is present below the inversion. Overland, if there is no cloud sheet, the radiational cooling leads to severe night frost and sometimes fog.

Anticyclones

The cloudy rainy weather of the depression is due to rising air, which is most pronounced near frontal regions. The anticyclone on the other hand is a large mass of descending or subsiding air. The subsiding motion takes place through nearly the whole depth of the troposphere but must obviously be checked near the Earth's surface, so that the lowest one or two thousand feet are little affected. Subsidence warms the air by compression (page 20); an inversion of temperature is produced within a few thousand feet of the ground and above the inversion the warming causes any cloud which may be present to evaporate away. Below the inversion, however, a sheet of Stratocumulus cloud often persists, especially in winter. The weather of an anticyclone is dry and settled. Generally winter anticyclones bring cold unpleasant, though dry, weather. At other seasons, however, the sunshine is powerful enough to dissipate fog and cloud, and, in summer, anticyclone weather is fine and warm.

Over the outer regions of an anticyclone the weather is dry, but the temperature and cloud depend on the air flow. Thus,

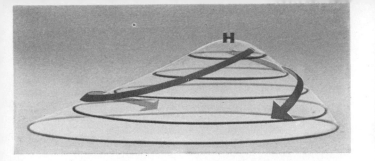

a winter anticyclone over Scandinavia will bring very cold air from Russia over most of western Europe; occasionally, as in the severe winters of 1947 and 1963, these conditions may persist for several weeks. On the other hand, an anticyclone over France and the Bay of Biscay in winter brings dry mild weather to the British Isles and much of northern Europe. Persistent winter anticyclones over Canada and the United States bring very low temperatures, but dry and often bright weather.

A **ridge of high pressure** is a wedge-shaped extension of an anticyclone or a belt of high pressure connecting two anticyclones. The weather is similar to that in an anticyclone. In temperate latitudes, ridges of high pressure often occur between two depressions and move with them; they give rise to intervals of fair weather, sometimes a whole day, in an otherwise unsettled period.

A **col** is the indefinite isobar configuration between two highs and two lows arranged alternately. It is a short-lived feature of the synoptic chart and no particular sort of weather can be attached to it, except that the winds are light.

Upper air synoptic charts

The features of synoptic charts so far discussed relate only to conditions near the surface. But it has been seen on page 18 that it is possible by means of radar and radio-sondes to measure pressure, temperature, humidity and wind up to high levels in the atmosphere. This is done for a network of stations twice or four times a day at fixed hours; the observations are reported in special codes and are distributed over the meteorological communications network and plotted on upper air synoptic charts in the forecasting offices.

Just as on the surface synoptic chart it is necessary to adjust the pressures to sea level, so the upper air **pressure charts** must be drawn each for one particular level. At first the charts were drawn for standard heights 1,000, 2,000, 3,000 ... metres above sea level; the plotted pressures in conjunction with the winds allowed upper air isobars to be drawn as on surface charts.

However, it is more convenient to plot the heights corresponding to standard values of pressure and to draw the contours (lines of equal height) of the pressure surface. In the forecasting services **contour charts** are usually drawn for standard pressure surfaces 700, 500, 300, 200 and 100 mb. These correspond approximately to 10,000, 18,000, 30,000,

40,000 and 50,000 feet above sea level. Contours are usually drawn at intervals of 60 metres (200 feet). The contour charts are, for all practical purposes, the same as charts of isobars for the same levels with the highs and lows precisely corresponding. The winds blow exactly along the contours and the strength for any latitude, is proportional to the contour gradient. Closely spaced contours, therefore, correspond to strong winds.

The difference between the heights of two standard pressure surfaces, say 1,000 and 500 mb, is called the thickness. The thickness is greatest when the air is warm because its density is then low and a relatively tall column of air is required to give the required 500 mb of pressure difference between its top and bottom. Charts showing contours of thickness are useful aids to forecasting and are called **thickness charts**. On these charts the highs are regions with warm air in depth and the lows are regions of cold air.

Contour charts of the pressure surface 500 mb *(left)*. *(Below)* corresponding thickness lines 1000 to 500 mb and selected sea level isobars. The unit of contour height and thickness is 10 metres.

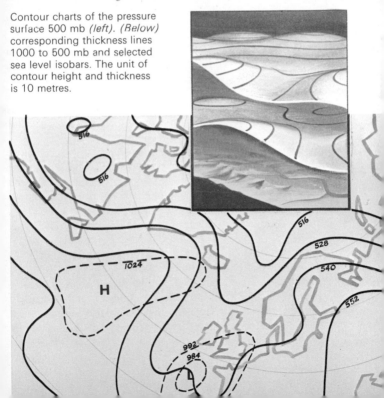

Relation of upper air to depressions, upper troughs and ridges

In the lower levels of the troposphere the contour patterns closely resemble the surface isobars, reproducing the highs and lows, troughs and ridges. At the higher levels the effect of temperature comes in to an increasing extent. There is a general tendency for high contour values to occur in low latitudes and vice versa – a general slope downwards from south to north is, so to speak, superimposed on the sea level pressure pattern. This has the effect of tending to smooth out the individual highs and lows. The usual pattern is a wave-like one consisting of a series of large ridges pointing polewards and troughs pointing equatorwards. These features are so large that a single trough-ridge pair covers 60° or even 90° of longitude. The whole hemisphere may be covered by six or fewer trough-ridge pairs.

The upper winds blow along the contours in accordance with Buys Ballot's Law (page 80) and, therefore, blow in a general west to east direction, though varying between north-northwest and south-southwest, as they pursue a wave-like course round the successive troughs and ridges. Similar troughs and ridges are shown on the thickness charts (page 93), the ridges, pointing polewards, having warm air within them and the troughs, pointing equatorwards, cold air. These features are slow moving and a region may remain under their influence for several days at a time.

Depressions tend to develop in the region between an upper trough and the next ridge to the eastward, especially near the extremities of the troughs and ridges. Anticyclones tend to develop between a ridge and the next trough to the eastward.

Surface depressions and anticyclones tend to move along the thickness lines in the same direction as the wind, but at much slower speeds. The situation is also complicated because the surface circulations alter the distribution of warm and cold air and hence change the upper patterns.

Jet streams appear on upper air charts as bands of closely spaced contours. Small depressions tend to move quickly along jet streams and to deepen where the contours fan out at the 'exit' end of the jet. A jet stream flowing over or directed towards a region usually implies unsettled weather there.

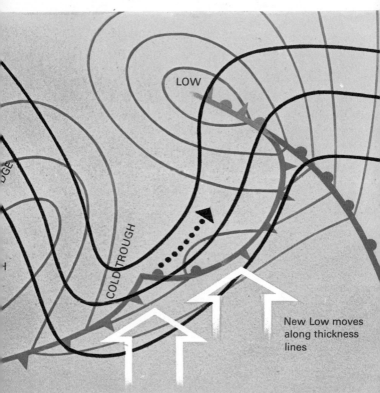

LOW

RIDGE

COLD TROUGH

H

New Low moves along thickness lines

New Low develops here

Warm front

Cold front

Occlusion

Thickness lines

Isobars

Thickness pattern, development and movement of depression

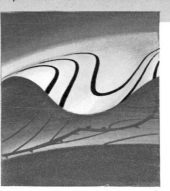

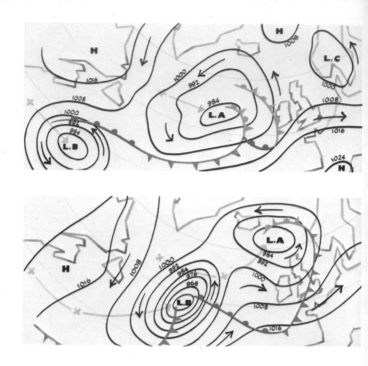

Techniques of forecasting – forecast charts

The forecasts dealt with in this section are for periods of twenty-four, or at most, forty-eight hours ahead. Long-range forecasting for a month or a season ahead uses different methods and is dealt with in a separate section.

The forecaster's tools are the plotted and analysed synoptic charts for the surface and upper levels. The problem of forecasting is in two parts. The first is to identify the various air masses, depressions, anticyclones, troughs and fronts and to estimate how they will move and develop during the period of the forecast. To rationalize this estimate he prepares a forecast chart, sometimes called a prebaratic or prognostic chart, which shows the estimated pattern of the isobars and positions of the fronts at the end of the forecast period. The second part of the problem is to specify the weather, cloud, rain, fog, frost and so on to be associated with the pressure

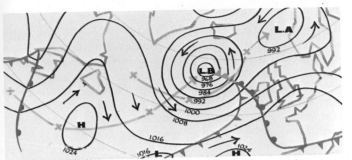

Sequence of synoptic charts showing movement of depression.
Tracks of centres and positions at 24 hr intervals are marked x——x.

systems, fronts and air masses. The individual radio-sonde observations provide information about the temperature and humidity of the air in depth; stability (page 22) is important in relation to the occurrence of fog, showers and thunderstorms, and the importance of humidity is obvious since appreciable rain cannot occur without an adequate supply of moisture.

It is not enough to study only the latest available synoptic chart, but the whole sequence over the past day or two. The development of the synoptic situation is a continuous process and the forecaster must keep a constant watch on it and study the evolving patterns. For example, in deciding how a depression is likely to move and develop over the next twenty-four hours, it is useful to have its track during the preceding twenty-four hours, together with a knowledge of its deepening or otherwise. Upper air charts are an essential aid for, as mentioned on page 95, they show the areas where depressions and anticyclones are likely to intensify or weaken, and the upper air contours provide useful guidance regarding the direction of movement of the surface systems.

The appropriate contour chart gives the distribution of wind speed and direction at any selected upper level and thereby provides essential information for the navigation of aircraft. For long flights, prognostic upper air charts are provided and these allow the operators to estimate fuel requirements – obviously these will be large if the aircraft is likely to encounter strong headwinds for most of the flight.

Forecasts for the press, radio and television

Nearly all readers of this book will be acquainted with weather forecasts through the press, radio and television. In most countries these carry forecasts which, in some cases, are exact copies of those issued by the official meteorological service; in others they are in paraphrase or précis form. Forecasts are supplied two or three times a day or even more frequently to these agencies; this is desirable because of the tendency of the weather to change quickly.

Radio forecasts are necessarily in verbal form only. To get the best from them the listener must attend carefully because the statements are often unavoidably complicated. If it is thought that this complication is unnecessary, let the reader try and put into a brief clear statement the weather of yesterday over an area only two or three hundred miles square, which he has the means of knowing exactly.

Radio and television forecasts *(left)* have one advantage over those appearing at the same time in newspapers *(right)* in that they can be based on more recent information. They suffer no delays due to printing and distribution.

Forecasts reproduced in the press and on television have the advantage that they can be illustrated by means of outline synoptic charts. These can be the most recent synoptic charts available and a forecast chart for a time towards the end of the forecast period. Isobars and fronts are the main features shown, usually with arrows indicating their direction of movement. This gives the reader or viewer simple charts enabling him to interpret the forecast and to understand what is happening if, later, the forecast is seen to be going wrong. The forecast positions of depressions and fronts are rarely exactly correct; possible errors of 100 miles in a twenty-four hour forecast have to be accepted, and with a front moving at twenty miles an hour, this would mean a five-hours error in the timing of the onset of rain. Forecast charts are particularly useful to travellers. Setting off in fine weather a traveller could easily deduce that he was likely to encounter bad weather on some distant part of his route.

Modern developments in forecasting

The development of electronic equipment in the past twenty years has provided new aids to weather forecasting. One of these is the transmission of **facsimile weather charts** by radio and land line. Before the introduction of facsimile, every forecasting station had to plot its own charts manually from the collective synoptic messages (page 74). Now it is possible for subsidiary forecasting stations to receive completely plotted and analysed charts from a few main centres. There is, for example, a facsimile interchange between Europe, North America and the western Pacific (Japan). The forecaster in the United Kingdom Headquarters can immediately see what his opposite number in the United States is thinking regarding the analysis of the current situation and the forecast chart (page 96); he can take advantage of the other man's local experience.

At the transmitting end the chart is scanned electronically and simultaneously reproduced on a sheet of sensitized paper at the receiving end; the important thing is that the receiving forecaster has a copy of the chart on paper for study.

The most important modern development is the preparation of forecast charts by calculation, made possible by electronic **computers**. The whole problem of weather forecasting is basically scientific – a problem of mathematical physics. For example, the wind system throughout the atmosphere depends on the pressure distribution; this in its turn is determined partly by the winds themselves which move the air about, partly by the density of the air, which itself is dependent on temperature, and so on. The point is that the laws connecting these quantities are numerical in nature and can be expressed mathematically. If the state of the whole atmosphere were known in sufficient detail at any moment of time, it is theoretically possible to calculate the state at any future moment – that is to calculate a weather forecast. But the problem is enormously complicated; far more complicated than problems in astronomy, which is conspicuously successful in predicting eclipses exactly for many years ahead. To compute a twenty-four hour forecast using pencil and paper would require many years work, which is absurd. However, with a large computer the forecast can be completed in a few hours, using data supplied in the routine synoptic messages.

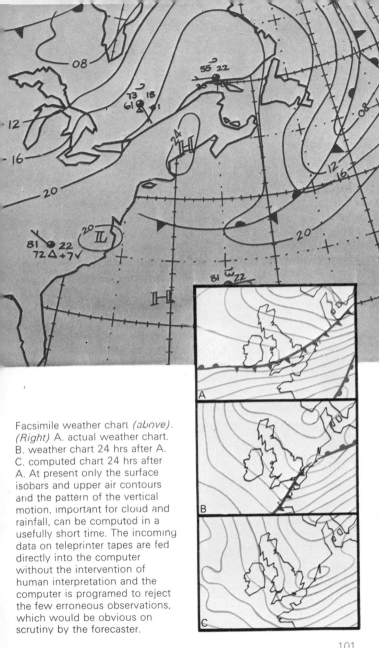

Facsimile weather chart *(above)*. *(Right)* A. actual weather chart. B. weather chart 24 hrs after A. C. computed chart 24 hrs after A. At present only the surface isobars and upper air contours and the pattern of the vertical motion, important for cloud and rainfall, can be computed in a usefully short time. The incoming data on teleprinter tapes are fed directly into the computer without the intervention of human interpretation and the computer is programed to reject the few erroneous observations, which would be obvious on scrutiny by the forecaster.

The use of **radar** for the detection of enemy aircraft came into prominence during the Second World War. Radar operates with radio waves of very short wave length; they travel with the speed of light, in straight lines and are reflected by metallic and other objects which conduct electricity. If a radar pulse is directed at such an object the reflected wave can be detected and the time interval between the emitted and return signals measured electronically, then the distance of the object from the radar station can be accurately calculated. The direction of the object is that in which the dish-like radar aerial must be pointed to receive the return signal. In practice, the distant object appears as a spot of light on a radar screen – resembling a television screen but circular in shape – with the radar station at the centre. Radar is useful in meteorology because raindrops and hailstones reflect the waves, so that distant rain showers and thunderstorms can be located on the screen. The radar aerial scans the surrounding region by rotating in a horizontal plane; the rain appears at the correct bearing and distance (to scale) as a light patch on the screen. Radar pictures taken at intervals of a few minutes show the movement of the rain. The intensity of the rain is shown by the intensity of the light on the radar screen.

Artificial **satellites** are devices carrying scientific instruments which circle the earth in regular orbits for long periods. They are outside the atmosphere; if not they would be

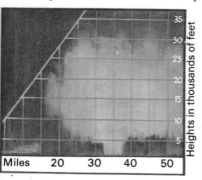

If the radar aerial is swung vertically, a picture of the distribution of rain through the depth of a shower or thundercloud is produced.

Radar pictures are particularly useful in estimating whether showers will pass over, or miss, important outdoor events and give a high degree of accuracy over two or three hours.

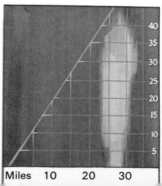

slowed down by air friction and could not maintain orbit. Their principal use in meteorology is the taking of photographs of cloud systems from very great heights. These photographs are transmitted to Earth and can be reproduced in a very short time by special receiving instruments. Before the days of satellites, forecasters relied for their knowledge of the existing clouds on the patchwork of observations made at the ground reporting stations and from these they had to produce the general picture. The satellite picture for example shows the whole cloud system of a depression with its fronts. It is especially useful over the oceans and sparsely populated land areas where observing stations are widely separated.

In remote areas it is too expensive to maintain manned observing stations and much research has been directed at designing **automatic stations**. At sea these stations would be mounted on anchored buoys. Elements like temperature, pressure and humidity have for many years been regularly observed by radio-sonde. Whereas, however, the radio-sonde is required to function for only an hour or two, an automatic station must do so for weeks and months without attention. Elements like visibility, cloud and rain present greater difficulties but these can be overcome. The stations report by radio at fixed hours or they can be interrogated by the parent station. Few stations are operating at present but they are expected to be used on an increasing scale in the future.

Satellites also carry instruments which measure radiation.

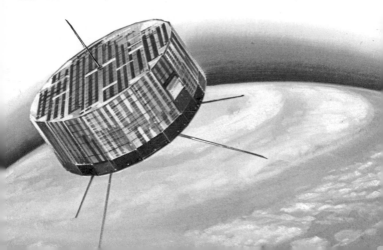

Long range forecasting means forecasting for periods longer than about a week; one month is the period usual in practice. The synoptic methods used on day to day forecasting cannot be extended beyond two to three days because after that time the weather is affected by systems, such as depressions which have not yet formed. For many years other methods have been experimented with but it cannot yet be said that there is a satisfactory method of long-range forecasting. Different methods are being tried in different countries; the simplest for the non-technical reader to understand is that used in the United Kingdom. It is called the Analogue Method – because it is based on the study of past weather situations analogous to the current one.

Suppose that at the end of December a forecast is being prepared for the following month, January. On an outline chart of the northern hemisphere are first plotted the differences between the average temperatures for that particular December and the average December temperature over a period of many years. These are called the temperature anomalies. Above normal temperatures are plotted in red, below normal in black and lines are drawn (in red and black) joining places where the

Specimen analogue charts over a period of 77 years:
Yellow=within 1 °C of normal   Green=1–2 °C below normal
Blue=2 °C or more below normal   Orange=1–2 °C above normal
Red=2 °C or more above normal

MAY 1968

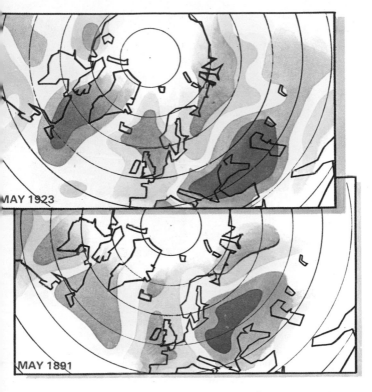

MAY 1923

MAY 1891

anomalies are the same (like contours or isobars). These form
a pattern for that particular month. Anomaly charts have been
prepared for each month back to the year 1880. The forecaster
looks through all the December charts of this series and picks
out a few which bear a close resemblance to the current month
of December. He then studies the weather of the Januaries
following these Decembers and, if these are similar, it is a fair
inference that the ensuing January will be similar also. The
process is, in fact, more complex than this because the forecaster also examines the sequences of depressions and anticyclones and general weather for those months. The essence
of the method is, however, that the forecaster searches for
similar situations in the past and works on the basis that the
current situation will evolve in a similar way.

In most hurricane areas *(above)*, adequate warning is given by the meteorological service. Most hurricanes occur in late summer and autumn, August to November in the northern and January to May in the southern hemisphere.

SPECIAL WEATHER SYSTEMS AND WINDS
Hurricanes (Tropical storms)

In the tropics, depressions, anticyclones and fronts such as occur in temperate and high latitudes are very ill-defined features, with one notable exception; that is the tropical storm. These occur in various parts of the tropical oceans under different names: thus, Hurricanes in the Caribbean, Cyclones in the Indian Ocean and Bay of Bengal, Typhoons in the China Seas and Willy-Willies off Australia. These are all basically the same kind of disturbance and for convenience will be referred to in this book under the common name hurricane.

Hurricanes are violent storm systems with very low pressure concentrated in a small area at the centre; the isobars are almost circular and the winds extremely violent. The winds circulate anticlockwise in the northern hemisphere, clockwise in the southern. The hurricane is about 300 or 400 miles in diameter and symmetrical, with the distribution of wind, cloud and weather the same all round its circular area. In its very centre, the hurricane has a circular area of light winds, no rain and clear sky or only very thin cloud; this region is called the 'Eye of the Storm'.

When the centre of a hurricane approaches within a few hundred miles there is increasing cirrus cloud and the barometer begins to fall slowly. As the centre gets nearer the cloud thickens and lowers, the wind begins to increase and rain starts to fall. Nearer the centre the wind increases to hurricane force, 60 knots, often much more; persistent wind speeds well over 100 knots have been recorded on many occasions. With severe hurricanes the wind speed is above the range which ordinary anemometers will record and the instruments are put out of action. The rain becomes torrential and the barometer falls very rapidly. Conditions become more and more violent right up to the edge of the eye. But then there is a sudden lull, the wind drops light, the rain ceases and the cloud thins markedly. The eye may be anything from 5 to 50 miles in diameter and affords a few minutes or even a few hours of quiet weather while it passes. From the air the eye appears as an enormous circular bowl of cloud. When it has passed, the storm is suddenly renewed in all its fury – cloud rain and wind as before except that the wind now blows from the opposite direction as is obvious from its circulation round the centre. Then the storm recedes, the rain and wind ease gradually and the barometer recovers quickly.

The hurricane winds cause enormous damage to buildings, power and telephone lines and vegetation. Another hazard is the high seas raised by the wind and tidal waves that sweep over low-lying coastal areas causing extensive flooding.

Tornadoes

Of all disturbances in the atmosphere, tornadoes are the most violent and destructive; fortunately they are quite small by atmospheric standards and the areas which they affect are very limited. A tornado is seen as a narrow writhing column of cloud apparently suspended from a thick dark cloud and reaching down to earth. Within and near the column the air is whirling round at very high speed. At the centre the air becomes rarefied under the influence of the centrifugal force, and its pressure falls to perhaps half the normal value. Wind speeds near the centre can only be estimated, for any measuring instruments are put out of action, but speeds up to 300 knots are probable. The central area of heavy damage is only about 100 yards across but, as the tornado moves, it leaves a long trail of complete destruction on a strip of about this width. Tornadoes occur at cold fronts when the warm air

The tremendous winds and flying objects associated with tornadoes *(left)* cause much loss of life of both men and animals. Waterspouts *(below left)* cause less damage because they can be seen and avoiding action taken. The strong winds that sometimes accompany dust storms *(below right)* cause the dust to penetrate the smallest crannies; delicate machinery is damaged both by penetration and abrasion.

is very damp and unstable. The worst tornadoes occur in the middle-west states of the United States in summer, and, to a lesser extent, in Australia. Less destructive tornadoes occur occasionally in Europe, South America and South Africa.

Waterspouts are similar to tornadoes but less violent and they occur over the sea. Whirling columns of air which occur in desert areas and suck up quantities of whirling sand are called **dust devils**. They are, in a sense, miniature tornadoes except that they develop from the ground upwards. They are due to atmospheric instability caused by intense heating.

Dust storms occur in dry desert areas when the rising currents associated with vigorous cold fronts lift large quantities of dust some hundreds of feet into the air. The appearance is of a large wall of dust advancing along the line of the front. The best known dust storms are those of the eastern Sahara and the Sudan where they are known as 'Haboobs'.

Monsoons

The name Monsoon means 'seasonal' and it is applied in particular to the rainy season of India. The monsoons arise from the great pressure changes which occur between winter and summer over the land mass of Asia (page 114). In winter and spring the whole continent is dominated by the Siberian anticyclone and the winds blowing round it and out of it are cold and dry. By June the Asiatic low pressure has developed and the winds off the warm ocean bring much cloud and rain. The change from hot dry to less hot rainy weather is usually sudden and the monsoon is then said to break.

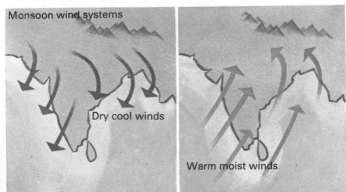

Monsoon wind systems

Dry cool winds

Warm moist winds

Special winds

Large scale wind flow patterns are modified by particular geographical and topographical features of the Earth's surface and give rise to characteristic local and regional winds.

Everybody has experience of the fresh cool breezes at the seaside in summer. The common explanation is that the air over the land becomes warmer, due to sunshine, than that over the sea. The warmer air rises and cool air from the sea flows in to take its place. This is true in a sense, but to cause a flow from sea to land a difference of pressure must be set up and rising air alone will not account for this. If the land warms up, air above it will increase in height; air originally below 1,000 feet will rise to a little above 1,000 feet and the pressure at 1,000 feet will rise. The resulting pressure difference at 1,000 feet will cause air to move from land to sea at that level, reducing the pressure at the surface over the land and increasing it over the sea. This pressure difference sets up the surface flow from sea to land, the cool **sea breeze**. At night when the land may cool below sea temperature, the effect is reversed, and there is a gentle drift of air from land to sea – the **land breeze**.

On a warm day the air in contact with a hill slope becomes heated and flows up the slope, giving rise to the Anabatic wind. If the hills are high enough the rising air may cool (by expansion) to its dew point, and the summits become capped

Land and sea breezes by day *(above)* and night *(below)*

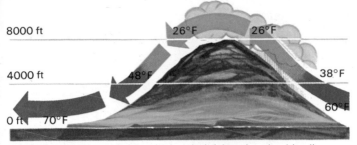

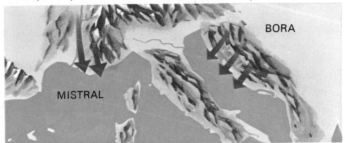

Formation of a warm dry mountain wind *(above)* and cold valley winds *(below)*

by clouds. At night the air in contact with the surface cools and flows down the slopes; this is called the **katabatic wind**.

The mistral of the Rhône Valley and adjacent parts of the French Riviera is the best known example of a **valley wind**. Air from the cold interior of Europe in winter is funnelled along the Rhône Valley, reaching great strength, which, combined with its low temperature, makes it notoriously unpleasant. The Bora is a similar cold wind flowing down the valleys to the head of the Adriatic.

When a current of damp air meets a mountain range it is forced to rise, and cloud and rain occur on the windward slopes. The temperature in the damp air falls at 3° F per 1,000 feet of rise (page 24). Descending on the leeward slope the air has now lost its moisture and its temperature rises at 5½° F per 1,000 feet of descent. If its rise and descent are each 10,000 feet it will arrive at the bottom of the lee slope 25° F warmer than at the same level on the windward side. This warm dry **mountain wind** is characteristic of the northern Alpine valleys where it is known as the Föhn. The Chinook is a similar wind in North America, east of the Rockies.

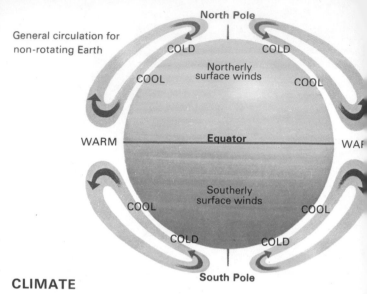

General circulation for non-rotating Earth

North Pole

COLD   COLD

Northerly
surface winds

COOL   COOL

WARM   Equator   WAR

Southerly
surface winds

COOL   COOL

COLD   COLD

South Pole

CLIMATE

The weather at any place changes daily, sometimes hourly. Climate is most simply described as the average weather over a period of many years, but for comparisons it is desirable to use figures. Thus, one talks about the average yearly rainfall, temperature, number of days on which rain falls and so on. For some purposes these averages are calculated monthly and this is sometimes more informative. For example, Edinburgh and New York have the same yearly average temperature, 47° F (8° C), but their temperatures in the coldest and hottest months are very different, thus:

Edinburgh   Jan 39° F (4° C), July 58° F (14·5° C)

New York   Jan 31° F (−0·5° C), July 74° F (23·5° C)

showing that New York has markedly hotter summers and colder winters than Edinburgh – a real climatic difference.

General circulation of the atmosphere

Climatic differences are caused in the first instance by the differing amounts of solar radiation received on different parts of the Earth's surface. If solar radiation were the only factor involved, all places in the same latitude would have the same average temperature. This, however, is far from being the case and another important factor is the world-wide system of winds which transport warm and cold air to very great distances from their source regions (page 82). The average world-wide wind system is called the general circulation of the atmosphere.

If the Earth did not rotate and its surface were smooth, the general circulation would be very simple. The temperature differences between the tropics and the poles would set up a circulation which is a magnified version of that described under land and sea breezes (page 110).

The effect of the Earth's rotation is to cause the winds to swing to their right in the northern hemisphere, to their left in the southern. In the northern hemisphere, the northward flowing upper winds from the tropics swing to become westerly; this happens in the subtropics at latitude 30° to 40° N. The accumulation of air in these latitudes produces a belt of high pressure at the surface. The southward flowing winds from the polar regions at the surface swing likewise to become easterlies. Between the polar and subtropical high pressures there is, on average, a belt of low pressure; this is caused by the frequent depressions which develop in the area but it is by no means permanent and is often interrupted by anticyclones. A similar arrangement of pressure belts occurs in the southern hemisphere. If they are respresented in a simple diagram the corresponding winds can be sketched in using Buys Ballot's Law to relate them to the isobars.

General circulation for rotating Earth

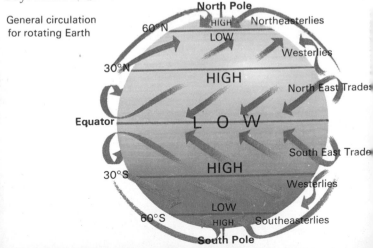

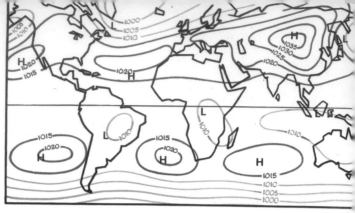

Average circulation patterns for January and July *(right)*

General circulation effects of land and sea

The last of the large scale factors affecting the general circulation is the distribution of land and sea. Land surfaces react quickly to radiation, becoming warm in summer, cold in winter. The oceans react far more slowly and during the summer they are cooler than the adjoining land, in winter they are warmer.

The effect of the surface is to produce relatively high pressure over cold areas and low pressure over warm ones, producing large modifications to the pressure and wind belts. Thus, over the great cold land mass of Asia and Europe, a winter anticyclone develops and completely masks the subtropical high pressure belt, which would otherwise appear. A weaker winter anticyclone appears over North America. In middle and high latitudes the warmest parts of the northern hemisphere in winter are the two great oceans and these, on average, are occupied by deep depressions called respectively

Major wind systems of the world for January and July *(right)*

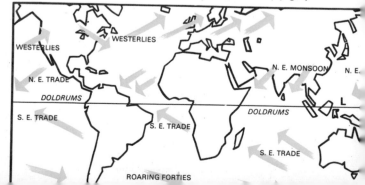

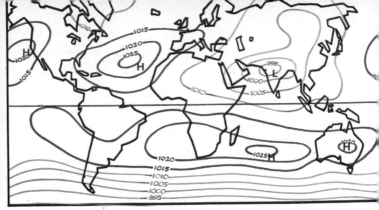

the Icelandic and Aleutian Lows. The subtropical highs over
the warm oceans are rather weak in winter. In summer the
land masses warm up; the Asiatic high of winter is replaced by
a large low pressure system with its centre over the hottest
part of the area, near northern India. Over the now relatively
cool oceans the Icelandic and Aleutian Lows weaken but the
subtropical high pressure centres become stronger. At all
seasons there is a belt of relatively low pressure near the
Equator but this tends to swing northward and southward
with the seasonal changes. The subtropical oceanic high
pressure cells tend to swing likewise.

In the southern hemisphere, owing to the seasonal differences, the effects are seen in reverse but they are much less
marked because there are no really big land masses. There are
slight tendencies for winter highs and summer lows over
South America, South Africa and Australia. But the main
feature is the permanence of the subtropical high pressure belt
over the oceans and the continuous belt of low pressure in
high southern latitudes.

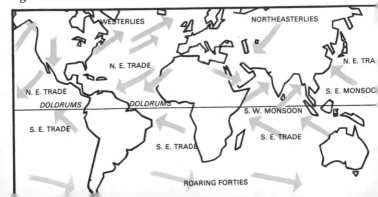

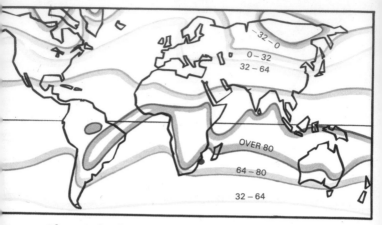

The winds obey Buys Ballot's Law (page 80) and can be readily sketched in from the isobars. The main *January* features are:

Prevailing south westerlies over the eastern parts of the North Atlantic and North Pacific and the adjacent parts of Europe and North America: The northeasterlies of China, Southeast Asia and India (the Northeast Monsoon (page 126): The Northeast Trades of the North Atlantic, North Pacific and Indian Oceans and the Southeast Trades of the southern part of these oceans.

and in *July*:

The continuous gradient of pressure from the high over the southern Indian Ocean to the low over northwest India giving southwest winds over India – the Southwest Monsoon. Note that these winds start as southeasterly in the southern hemisphere but, following Buys Ballot's Law, turn southwesterly on crossing the Equator: The strong westerlies in the far south: these also occur, a little weaker, in January and are known as the 'Roaring Forties'.

World distribution of temperature

Average temperature is approximately half way between the averages of day maximum and night minimum temperatures. Afternoon temperatures will, on the whole, be higher than those indicated, night temperatures lower. In *January*, the

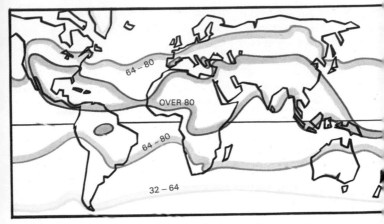

Distribution of average temperature for January *(left)* and July

lowest temperatures occur over the northern continents, northeast Siberia and northern Canada. The North Pacific and North Atlantic are warm and the prevailing westerly winds carry the warmth to the adjacent land, in particular into Europe. In North America, the Rocky Mountains block the penetration of oceanic winds and winter mildness is confined to the western coastal strip. Eastern coastal areas, on the other hand, have prevailing winds from the cold continental interiors and are much colder than at corresponding latitudes on the western coasts. The warmest areas are the land masses of the southern hemisphere, particularly South Africa and Australia.

In *July*, the northern continents are strongly heated. The hottest regions are the desert areas of the Sahara, Arabia, northwest India and California with average temperatures over 90° F (32° C). The line for 60° F which represents the summer temperature of southern Britain extends far to the north over Scandinavia, Siberia and Canada showing the influence of the heated land. Latitude for latitude the western coasts are somewhat cooler than the eastern.

It might be thought that the highest temperatures would occur along the equator. In fact they are found in latitudes 20° to 30° N and S. These are in the subtropical high pressure belt where the weather is dry and the sunshine prolonged.

The Equator is on the whole a cloudy region with a good deal of rain; vegetation is luxuriant and much of the Sun's heat is thus used up in evaporating moisture.

World distribution of rainfall

The charts below show the average yearly totals of rainfall, and the monthly averages for January and July.

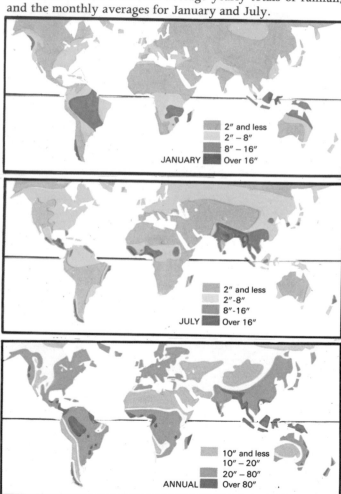

JANUARY
2" and less
2" – 8"
8" – 16"
Over 16"

JULY
2" and less
2"-8"
8"-16"
Over 16"

ANNUAL
10" and less
10" – 20"
20" – 80"
Over 80"

The highest rainfall totals occur near the Equator; this is to be expected because average pressure is low and temperature high, the air therefore having a high capacity for water vapour. Most of the rainfall in the Equatorial belt is convective (page 58), with prolonged heavy showers and frequent thunderstorms. High mountains cause an orographic effect in addition (page 58). The world's highest yearly rainfall, 425 inches, occurs at Cherrapunji in the mountains of northeast India. In very high latitudes rainfall is low because the air is too cold to contain much water vapour. The subtropical high pressure belts are naturally regions of low rainfall; they contain the great deserts of the Sahara, Southern Africa, California and Australia. The temperate belts have moderate rainfall on the western sides of the continents, Europe and North America, but the amounts fall off in the interior of Asia because it is so far from the sea.

The main feature of the January and July maps is the south to north shift, with the Sun, of the Equatorial rain belt. In *January* it covers Brazil, southern central Africa and northern Australia; in *July*, Central America, West Africa, the Sudan, northern India and southeast Asia. In the intervening months it shifts gradually between these south and north extremes.

In this section only the broad world patterns are considered; there are many small scale variations due to regional and local factors, but they are too numerous to describe here.

Desert climate

Deserts are areas where the rainfall is too low to maintain any vegetation at all, or only very scanty scrub, and any form of agriculture is impossible. The rainfall in desert areas is less than about 10 inches per year, often much less, and in some places several years may pass without any rain at all. The hot deserts are situated in the subtropical high pressure belts (page 114). In the northern hemisphere they are the Sahara, Arabia, large parts of Iraq and Iran, northwest India and California; in the southern hemisphere, South Africa (Kalahari) and a large part of Australia. Exceptionally in northern Kenya and Somaliland there is a large desert area quite near the Equator.

The deserts have almost unbroken sunshine for much of the

year and, except in winter, the days are extremely hot; maximum temperatures of over 110° F (42° C) are common. The temperature falls rapidly at night, though in summer it remains quite warm; in the winter half-year night temperatures may fall to freezing point or a little below. The air is always very dry; this makes the heat bearable and the climate is not unhealthy. Certainly it is less oppressive than the less hot but moist climates nearer the Equator. Rainfall is very rare but occasionally falls in short heavy storms; then the dry sand valleys (wadis) are filled with rushing torrents and there is local short-lived flooding. The water soon soaks away but is useful in maintaining the underground water which supplies

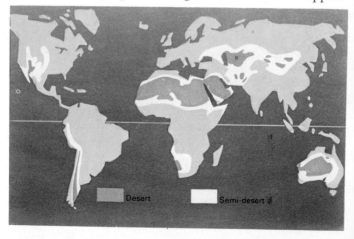

Desert   Semi-desert

wells and supports the vegetation of the oases. Sand and dust are raised by the wind; the finer dust particles to great heights, and dust-storms (page 108) are common; the sand is deposited in rippled dunes and rocks are abrased into fantastic shapes by the wind-borne sand. The remaining great desert is the Gobi in Mongolia. Though very hot in summer, it shares the very cold winters of central Asia.

Semi-desert areas include the Steppes of southern Russia and central Asia and the Prairies of Canada. These are regions with dry, very cold winters but warm in summer with enough rainfall to support the growing of cereals, especially wheat.

Hot moist climates

The climate of the equatorial belt is, for the most part, hot and humid. There is abundant rainfall, mostly in heavy showers and thunderstorms, but also a good deal of sunshine – conditions which favour luxuriant vegetation. A substantial part of the Sun's heat is used up in evaporation so that temperatures are not so high as in the hot deserts; the afternoon maximum averages about 90° F (32° C), and 100° F is extremely rare; the corresponding figures for the hot deserts are 110° F and 125° F. The moist atmosphere checks radiative loss of heat from the ground so nights are warm with minimum temperatures 70-75° F (21-23° C). This high level of temperature is maintained with little variation throughout the year. The seasons, so far as they do exist, are distinguished not as warm and cold but by variation of rainfall and cloudiness. Rain falls at all times of the year, but more especially at the time of overhead Sun; on the Equator this occurs in March and September. Farther from the Equator the two rainy periods tend to merge into one; May to July in the northern, November to January in the southern hemisphere. For those used to temperate climates, living conditions are trying because of the heat combined with the high humidity. Formerly the climate was unhealthy because the hot stagnant swamps were the breeding places of insect carriers of infection, and diseases like malaria and yellow fever were rife. The Guinea Coast of West Africa was known as the 'White Man's Grave. Now, with improved drainage and hygiene and combative measures against the mosquito, the Equatorial climate is quite healthy, though enervating, and air-conditioning has greatly improved indoor comfort. On the coasts, sea breezes bring some relief from the humid heat.

The principal regions with an Equatorial climate are the Amazon Basin in South America, West Africa and the Congo Basin, Malaya and the East Indies. Inland the country is covered with dense hardwood forest or jungle. The coasts are palm-fringed or consist of mangrove swamps, the latter especially in the deltas of the Amazon and Niger.

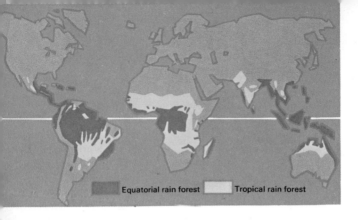

Equatorial rain forest | Tropical rain forest

Savannah

Between the rainy Equatorial belt and the desert regions on either side are the regions known as Savannahs. They have a single rainy season about the period of overhead Sun, May to August in the northern, November to February in the southern hemisphere. The rest of the year is dry. Vegetation consists mostly of scrub and grass, which turns brown during the long dry season, interspersed with isolated trees. The wetter parts of the region support crops such as ground-nuts and sisal; there are some cattle and sheep but the rainfall is unreliable and droughts cause great losses in some years.

Comparison of Equatorial rain forests *(left)* with savannah

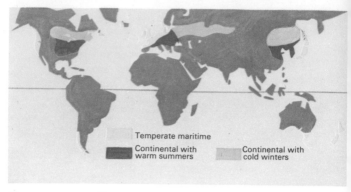

Temperate maritime

Continental with warm summers

Continental with cold winters

Temperate climates

Temperate climates are those which do not have extremes, either of hot or cold, wetness or dryness, and they allow ordinary human activities to be carried on – at least for most of the year – without great discomfort or inconvenience. The changes between summer and winter are stimulating, and yet not so extreme as to be frustrating, and it is probably no accident that the most highly developed communities lie in the temperate zones, notably in Europe and North America.

There are two varieties of temperate climate, maritime and continental. The **maritime climate** is strongly influenced by the oceans, which maintain fairly steady temperatures, remaining relatively warm in winter and cool in summer. Since the prevailing winds are westerly in the temperate zone the oceanic influence is carried inland on the western sides of the land masses. This is particularly marked in Europe where

Summer and winter scenes of temperate climates *(above and bottom left)*

mountain barriers run mostly from west to east thus allowing winds from the ocean to penetrate far into the interior. On the other hand, in North America the Rocky Mountains running from north to south restrict the oceanic influence to the westernmost states of the United States and Canada. The weather is characteristically changeable with warm and cold, wet and dry spells lasting several days, but rarely longer. Except on the high ground the snow of winter and early spring does not lie very long. In western Europe the winters are, as a rule, particularly mild for the latitude because the northeast Atlantic is abnormally warm. In the southern hemisphere the outstanding example of a temperate maritime climate is that of New Zealand, relatively small islands in a vast ocean area.

The influence of the ocean decreases towards the east in North America and Europe, and the climate becomes more **continental** with hotter summers and more severe winters. Rivers are frozen and snow lies for long periods in winter but the snow is dry and powdery and less of a nuisance than the wet slushy snow of the milder west. In spring when the snow and ice melt there is a short unpleasant interval of mud, slush and floods. Large scale agriculture can be carried on but the growing season is shorter than in the west. Occasionally in winter a long spell of east winds sets in over western Europe, bringing with it prolonged cold and snow of the continental winter, as in 1947 and 1963.

Polar and Arctic climates

The polar regions are perpetually covered by ice and snow. During the long summer days – six months continuous daylight at the Poles – the sun is too low in the sky to cause appreciable melting and the temperature rarely gets above freezing point. The long polar night is a period of intense frost. The lowest air temperatures at the Earth's surface have been recorded in Antarctica, well below $-100°$ F $(-73°$ C). The north polar region is covered by the frozen Arctic Ocean, effectively a vast plain covered with snow except where the ice is laid bare by the winds. Antarctica, on the other hand, is a great mountainous continent covered with ice, in places many thousands of feet thick. Human life in the normal sense is impossible in these frozen regions. During the last twenty years, however, scientific parties of many nations have become established in Antarctica; a United States base has been established at the South Pole itself, living under the ice surface. All food, fuel and equipment have to be taken in by

air. Apart from the extreme cold the main hazards are the fearsome blizzards, winds of gale force with driving drifting snow which make outdoor activity impossible. In the northern hemisphere the ice cap which covers almost the whole of Greenland is very similar to Antarctica.

For much of the year northern Canada and northern Siberia also have polar climates. But for a short period in summer these land masses warm up and, with southerly winds, temperatures occasionally reach 80° F (27° C) though the average is only about 40° F (4° C). These are the Tundra regions which carry a poor vegetation of moss and lichen, providing food for reindeer which support primitive communities. In Siberia there has been considerable industrial development, but special precautions have to be taken in building because the ground at a small depth below the surface is, in nature, permanently frozen, sometimes to a depth of many hundred feet; if this layer is melted by heat from the buildings, it could cause subsidence.

Mediterranean climate

This is a special type of climate expressed shortly as 'summer drought, winter rain' which occurs in various parts of the world in middle latitudes, notably the Mediterranean, from which it gets its name. It arises from the annual shift, with the Sun, of the subtropical high pressure belt and the temperate latitude low pressure (page 114). In the northern hemisphere in summer the subtropical high moves north to affect the Mediterranean and corresponding latitudes elsewhere; in winter these areas come under the influence of the temperate latitude depressions, as may be seen from the maps on pages 114 and 115. The Mediterranean Sea itself being cool in summer and warm in winter tends to enhance this pressure effect. These changes give rise to the well-known fine sunny warm summers of the Mediterranean and compratively rainy stormy winters. By contrast, many parts of the world have at least as much rain in summer as in winter; some have more. Other areas enjoying the Mediterranean type of climate are California, South Africa and the southern parts of Australia.

Comparative diagram of rainfall and temperature for holiday areas

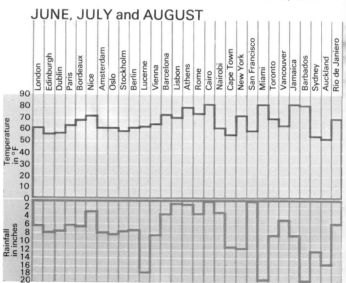

JUNE, JULY and AUGUST

Weather and holidays

The most popular holiday areas are obviously those where the climate offers a good chance of warmth and sunshine, without uncomfortable heat. For Europe these features can be most reliably expected in the Mediterranean, and for the Soviet Union on the Black Sea Coast; for the United States, California and Florida. The tropics for much of the year are too hot for comfort, and the Equatorial regions can be very trying on account of the humidity. In the subtropics, for example the Caribbean, the best season is winter with the relatively cool dry trade winds; the summers are hot and humid. Very pleasant summer weather often occurs in the more northerly parts of Europe and the United States but it cannot be relied upon and cool rainy spells are frequent. In the southern hemisphere the southernmost parts of South America, Africa and Australia are the most comfortable regions. Other suitable holiday areas are the eastern seaboard of South Africa and lowland Chile.

Mountain climate

The types of climate described so far are determined largely by latitude and proximity to the oceans, but they apply only to areas fairly near to sea level. The variation from tropical to polar climates is a gradual one, spread over a distance of several thousand miles. In mountainous areas in the tropics this same variation of climate occurs in a vertical distance of about four miles. The foothills may be covered by the dense steamy Equatorial rain forest, the summits, permanently snow-covered, are as inhospitable as the polar regions themselves. Between, there are the variations of climate that go with the decrease of temperature from sea level upwards.

Mountainous areas, except in desert regions, usually have abundant (orographic) rainfall (page 58) at levels below the snow-line. Higher up the rainfall decreases because the air is too cold to contain much moisture. Despite the high rainfall, however, vegetation is abundant only in favoured places where there is sufficient depth of soil and shelter from the strong winds which are characteristic of exposed mountain areas. The sequences of vegetation with altitude for tropical and temperate mountain areas are illustrated on this page.

Aspect is an important factor in mountain climates. Sun-facing slopes (south in the northern hemisphere) are genial, north-facing slopes, comparatively bleak, a point that should be borne in mind in choosing a place to live in in temperate latitudes, even on comparatively small hills.

The level of permanent snow, or snow-line, varies with the latitude.

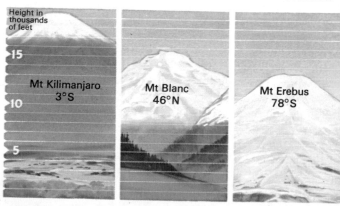

Height in thousands of feet

15

10

5

Mt Kilimanjaro
3°S

Mt Blanc
46°N

Mt Erebus
78°S

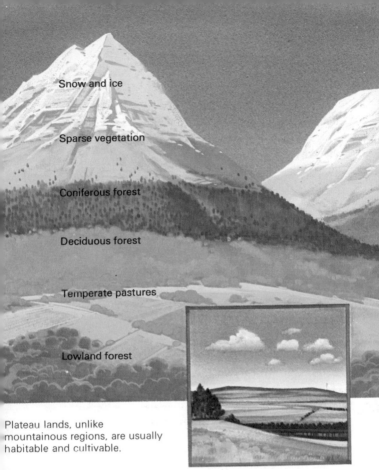

Snow and ice

Sparse vegetation

Coniferous forest

Deciduous forest

Temperate pastures

Lowland forest

Plateau lands, unlike mountainous regions, are usually habitable and cultivable.

Plateau climate

A plateau is a large comparatively flat area at a high altitude. Unlike the rugged mountains it is, unless too high and cold, habitable and cultivable. Perhaps the most interesting plateau areas are in Africa, in particular the Highlands of Kenya, astride the Equator. There, at heights of 6,000 to 8,000 feet above sea level, the climate is pleasant, like a European summer and temperate latitude types of farming are carried on. Above about 8,000 feet the reduced atmospheric pressure causes slight shortness of breath and loss of energy, at least for those accustomed to living near sea level.

131

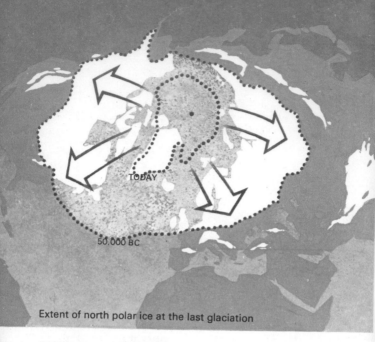

Extent of north polar ice at the last glaciation

Climate in the past

Our knowledge of climate in the remote past is derived from geological evidence and the study of fossils. The earth has existed for hundreds of millions of years; most of that time characterized by alternate ice ages and warm intervening periods. An **ice age** occurs when the polar ice caps spread over a substantially larger area. The last of several ice ages began about 60,000 BC and finally disappeared about 8,000 BC. There were also warm periods. The coal measures of Britain, Europe and North America are the remains of tropical swamp vegetation from a climate much warmer than the present.

During early historic times climatic evidence consists of legend and writings in which reference to the weather was only incidental. Observation of the weather only began about 500 years ago and became systematic only in the last century. In northwest Europe it is known that the period about 400 BC was comparatively genial; the Dark Ages, around 700 AD, were colder and wetter than today and about the twelfth century AD the vine flourished in parts of England. Climate deteriorated

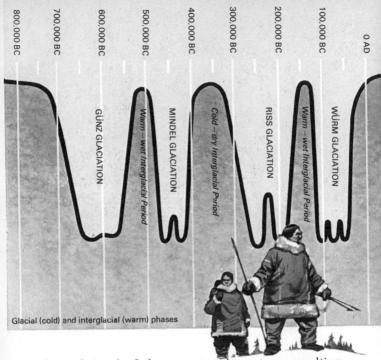

Glacial (cold) and interglacial (warm) phases

(chart labels, left to right:)

800,000 BC

700,000 BC
GÜNZ GLACIATION

600,000 BC
Warm – wet Interglacial Period

500,000 BC
MINDEL GLACIATION

400,000 BC
Cold – dry Interglacial Period

300,000 BC

200,000 BC
RISS GLACIATION

Warm – wet Interglacial Period

100,000 BC
WÜRM GLACIATION

0 AD

again about the end of the seventeenth century, resulting in large scale abandonment of farming, and famine in Scotland.

In the past hundred years, there has been a minor fluctuation in Britain. Of the twenty years 1880–1899 there were no fewer than fourteen really severe winters. From 1900 to 1939 there were only two, 1917 and 1929. These forty years were characterized by mild winters which had their effect on building practice – there was much outside plumbing. Since 1940 the winter temperature appears to have deteriorated; 1940, 1941 and 1942 were all severe, 1947 was the worst for over 100 years and 1963 the worst for 200 years. Of course there have been mild winters in between but, on the whole, winter temperature seems to be falling. In the winter of 1967–68 Arctic ice to the north of Iceland was more extensive than since 1940. Whether this is a permanent or minor fluctuation is too early to say, but does seem that the run of mild winters from 1900 to 1940 were exceptional and the experience of the last twenty-five years is the more normal.

WEATHER AND MAN
Weather and agriculture

Man ultimately depends for his livelihood on the growing of crops for food, whether these are used directly or as fodder for meat-producing animals. In prehistoric times man gathered his food where he found it and there was no attempt at cultivation. In the course of time primitive agriculture developed. **World distribution** of crops is conditioned by the fertility of the soil and the climate.

Taking the broad view, crops may be divided into four main classes. The first is that requiring tropical climates and includes tropical fruits like bananas, coffee, tea, sugar, rice, rubber and cotton. The requirement is high temperature and adequate rainfall. Temperature must be high throughout the year; some of these crops would grow well in the summer of central Europe, but could not survive the winter.

The second group consists of citrus fruits, olives and vines. Citrus fruits and olives thrive in the Mediterranean type of climate which, has cool, moist, but not frosty, winters and hot summers. The vine can, however, stand a certain amount of winter frost – hence its cultivation in central Europe.

The third group consists of the temperate latitude cereals,

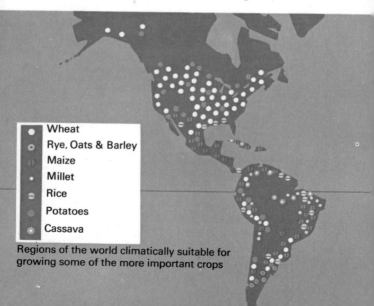

Wheat
Rye, Oats & Barley
Maize
Millet
Rice
Potatoes
Cassava

Regions of the world climatically suitable for growing some of the more important crops

wheat, barley, oats and rye, vegetables and root crops. These are annual crops, that is, the plants do not as a rule survive the winter but must be renewed by sowing each spring. In those parts with mild winters, for example western Europe and western North America, wheat and green vegetables are not killed by winter conditions but these circumstances are exceptional. Warm or hot summers are required for wheat. With spring sowing, winter conditions do not matter.

The fourth group consists of forest trees. These occur in all regions except those with desert and polar climates. Some broad groups may be distinguished. The Equatorial rain forests produce hard woods like teak and mahogany. Sub-tropical and temperate latitudes produce a great variety of trees both deciduous and evergreen, used mostly for timber. In higher latitudes these gradually give way to conifers, supplying soft wood and wood pulp for newsprint.

In mountainous areas, climate and crops depend to some extent on altitude. In the tropics all types of climate, from tropical to polar, occur in succession on the slopes of high mountains. In East Africa because of these altitude differences, tropical fruits like bananas and temperate latitude fruits like apples and plums can be grown within a few miles of each other – and as novelties in the same garden.

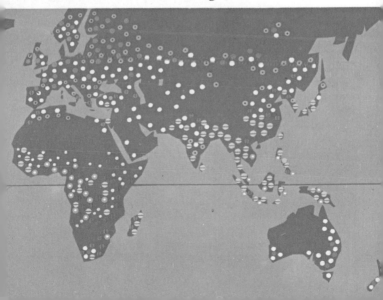

Weather information for agriculture

In the developed countries agricultural practice has grown out of long experience and it can hardly be said that climatic studies add much to the farmer's knowledge of the suitability of particular regions for particular crops. However, such studies are useful for assessing the agricultural potential of undeveloped areas. In some tropical regions, for example, the rainfall is not sufficient for a particular crop in every year. Climatic studies enable prospective growers to estimate the risk before committing themselves to a large outlay.

The daily weather forecasts are of help to the farmer in planning his work, but these forecasts at present are valid at most for two or three days. In summer, especially during the periods of haymaking and harvest, special forecasts of fine weather are issued to farmers, when the meteorological situation is considered to justify them: such forecasts have proved very helpful. Another hazard for which daily forecasts are useful is frost. The citrus fruit-growing industry, particularly in California, is vulnerable to this spring hazard, and timely warning enables protective measures to be taken.

Meteorological advice has found its most useful application in connection with certain diseases of farm animals and crops, some of which depend as regards severity on the weather of an earlier period. In Britain the best example is potato blight. This disease breaks out quickly and generally in areas where, for an unbroken period of forty-eight hours, warm, very humid weather occurs. The occurrence of such conditions is, of course, known immediately from the network of meteorological reporting stations. The farming community on being warned can take prompt and effective preventive action by spraying. If the conditions do not occur, spraying is not necessary thus saving spray material and effort.

Weather and aviation

The aviation industry has been for many years probably the greatest single user of meteorological services. All large airports have a meteorological office for providing advice to aircrews and observing the local weather at frequent intervals. In addition, the meteorological services provide climatological advice for the planning of airfield locations.

Areas affected by migrating locust swarms

Breeding areas

Large areas of the subtropics suffer serious crop losses due to locusts. Studies by the World Meteorological Organization have led to the conclusion that swarms travel with the winds and daily weather charts indicate wind change and thus, locust movement. Aircraft control swarms by spraying them with insecticide.

137

An airfield must obviously be located on nearly level ground and must be free from obstructions such as hills and tall buildings along the directions of landing and take-off. It must be as free as possible from fog and very low cloud. Climatological statistics of these factors are used as far as possible in **selecting airfield sites**. If there is no meteorological station near a proposed site, one is set up specially to collect information for a period of at least two or three years before work on the site begins. Meteorological statistics for existing and planned airfields are compiled with particular reference to fog and low cloud amount and height.

An aircraft must land and take off as nearly as possible into wind; cross winds of more than about 20 knots may be dangerous. The **alignment of runways** is, therefore, in the directions of the winds which occur most frequently. This is done with the aid of a wind rose – a diagram based on several years' observation showing the percentage frequencies of winds from various directions.

In the **design of aircraft** to operate on particular routes, for example to cross the Atlantic, engine power and fuel capacity are obviously important considerations. In particular, fuel load at take-off must be kept as low as is possible consistent with safety, for excess fuel can be carried only at the

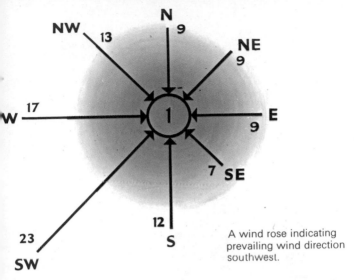

A wind rose indicating prevailing wind direction southwest.

expense of pay-load in the form of passengers or cargo. The most important factor in the estimation of the necessary fuel capacity is the strength of head winds. These occasionally reach 80 to 100 knots and may add substantially to the time taken on the flight, with consequently increased fuel requirements. Climatological statistics of winds over the routes which a new aircraft will operate provide the necessary information.

Before setting out on a long flight the pilot needs information about the **winds** at flying level over the route. This is given in a forecast chart of upper air contours. For a flight from London to New York the contour chart would cover western Europe, the North Atlantic and eastern North America. The winds can be deduced from the contours (page 92) so the winds have been marked in on the illustrative chart on page 138. This enables the pilot to estimate the average head wind over the direct route – hence the time of flight and fuel requirements. Alternatively it enables him to judge whether fuel and time would be saved by taking a less direct route in order to encounter lighter head winds. Three routes are shown on the chart, and it is clear that the northernmost route, though longer, will have more favourable winds.

Fog and very low cloud are the main **hazards** at airfields and sometimes are so bad as to prevent landing. On long

Modern aircraft are equipped with radar to detect hazards in their flight path, especially thunder clouds *(left)* which can give a severe buffeting.

flights pilots are warned by radio of such conditions at their destination and provision is always made for landing at an alternative place. The alternate may be some hundreds of miles away; thus for eastward transatlantic flights Prestwick in Scotland is often used as alternate when London Airport is fog-bound. With the development of automatic landing devices, fog and low cloud are becoming less of a hazard.

Under certain conditions, heavy deposits of ice form, particularly on the wings and tailplane of aircraft in flight and, if allowed to accumulate, will lead to dangerous overloading and loss of control. Equipment is provided in the design of the aircraft to prevent these dangerous build-ups, but the risk is best avoided and here meteorological knowledge is helpful. Ice forms rapidly when an aircraft flies through a cloud consisting of supercooled water drops at temperatures below freezing (page 56) or when it flies in freezing air through rain falling from a warmer layer above. The pilot will normally have been warned of these conditions in his forecast and can, therefore, avoid them. If he meets icing unexpectedly he can take avoiding action by changing the flight level (and hence the air temperature) or flying out of the clouds. The greater parts of long distance flights today are carried out at levels above the weather and icing risk is confined to climb and descent.

Thunder clouds should be avoided by aircraft at all costs, not because of the danger from lightning strikes, which is negligible, but because of the violent turbulence, up and down current, and possibly **hail**. The vertical currents may cause the aircraft to gain or lose height by several thousands of feet in a minute or two; this may be fatal in mountainous country. The up and down currents are only a few hundred feet across; a fast aircraft passes through several of them in a matter of seconds and receives a severe buffeting which in an extreme case may cause it to break up. Fortunately, thunder clouds can be seen far enough away for pilots to avoid them, and modern aircraft are also equipped with radar for detection.

Occasionally an aircraft receives a severe buffeting while flying in clear air when there is no sign visible to the pilot. Not much is known about it at present and it cannot be reliably forecast. It is liable to occur downwind of high mountain ranges and near jet streams, but serious **clear air turbulence** is very rare.

Weather and shipping

Seafarers have for long been the most weather-conscious of any single section of the community. For centuries, the crews of Arab dhows sailing between East Africa, the Persian Gulf, and India used their knowledge of the steady Indian Ocean trade winds for successful voyaging. In the great days of sailing ships, a world wide knowledge of the earth's wind systems was acquired and these were mapped as aids to navigation. Synoptic meteorology, that is, forecasting using weather maps, was begun in the middle of the last century by naval authorities in an effort to obtain warnings of storms which frequently were the cause of shipping disasters.

Modern shipping is less affected by weather than were sailing ships; nevertheless, **weather services** are necessary for their successful commercial operation and sometimes for their safety. For this reason, maritime countries broadcast special weather information for the use of shipping. These include synoptic reports from which the ships' officers may construct weather charts for their own locality, warnings of adverse weather particularly gales and fog. These enable precautions to be taken, depending on the size of the ship.

Ship routing is a recent development which can save time and money on ocean voyages. Any ship will obviously be slowed by strong head winds, equally it will be slowed by the high waves which the strong winds generate. There is now a service operated in conjunction with the forecasting services which tells the ship's master either the route which will enable him to complete the voyage in the shortest time, or the best course to set over the next twenty-four hours or so, in the light of the expected condition of wind and sea. In some recent cases, ships have been advised to use a North Atlantic crossing some hundreds of miles longer than the most direct route, resulting in a saving of 12 to 24 hours on the crossing, with a large saving of costs.

Our knowledge of ocean weather has been built almost entirely on meteorological observations by **merchant ships**. There are now many hundreds of ships which report regularly by radio, on a voluntary basis, for which the meteorological services owe them a great debt. All the observations are entered in log books which are studied and summarized. From these data a knowledge of the climate of the ocean areas has been built up and published in tables and atlases; these, with the ordinary land station data, complete the world picture. The ships' observations are the source of information regarding ocean currents which have also been mapped.

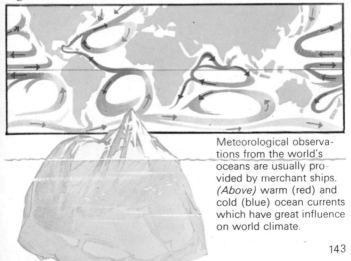

Meteorological observations from the world's oceans are usually provided by merchant ships. *(Above)* warm (red) and cold (blue) ocean currents which have great influence on world climate.

Weather and public services

Public services, such as transport, power supplies, water supply and drainage, operate more efficiently and with less inconvenience to the users if they are provided with reliable weather information.

With **roads and railways** it is largely a question of good forecasts. On the roads the chief hazards are ice, snow and fog. Little can be done about fog except perhaps to warn travellers not to take unnecessary journeys. Ice and snow can be guarded against by timely warning, enabling gritting or snow clearance to be put into operation. On the railways the hazards are fog and frozen points and precautions can be taken against these if warnings are received in time. Electrified railways taking power from a third rail are especially vulnerable to icing. A coat of ice on the conductor rail prevents the locomotive taking up the current and even though it may occur only locally, it may disorganize a whole system where traffic is intense. Special trains are run to coat the conductor

Timely warnings can prevent unnecessary dislocation of road and rail services by ice and snow.

The size of dams and reservoirs *(top right)* depends on the inflow of water from a large catchment area. This can be assessed from a knowledge of rainfall over the area. They must be large enough to cater for all but the severest droughts. Occasional falls determine the size of a dam and spillway.

rail with de-icing fluid when this hazard is threatened, but they are very costly, and reliable forecasts, if only preventing their unnecessary use, can save much money.

Climatic data are useful in the planning of motorways, especially in hilly districts. Among other factors, freedom from fog and snow is important. Where the older data are insufficient, special observing posts have been set up at intervals on possible routes before a final decision is reached.

The demand for gas and electricity fluctuates violently as the weather changes; in cold and dull weather the demand on **power supplies** is high; in warm bright weather it is much less; in changeable weather it fluctuates hourly. Electricity cannot be stored and the supply authorities need weather information at about hourly intervals. Gas can be stored and forecasts covering two or three days enable the manufacturer of gas to be adjusted to the probable demand. Similar forecasts are helpful to authorities in deciding when plant can be taken out of operation for maintenance purposes.

Climatic studies are helpful in the design of **water supplies**, that is reservoirs, dams and drainage systems. Town drainage systems must be designed to get rid quickly of the water which falls in heavy storms, the heaviest storm which is likely to occur once in, say, ten, twenty or fifty years, which can be estimated from past data. It would obviously be too expensive to cater for the heaviest conceivable storm.

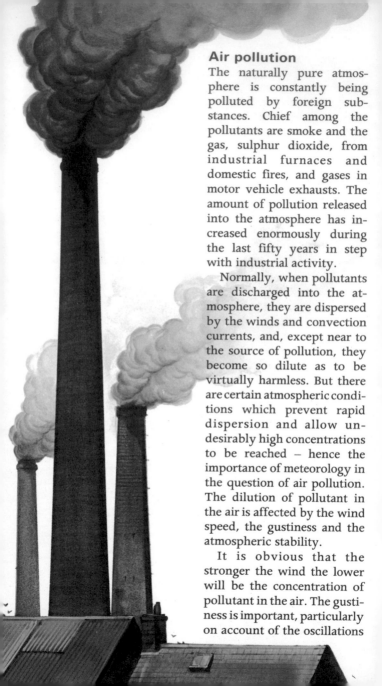

Air pollution

The naturally pure atmosphere is constantly being polluted by foreign substances. Chief among the pollutants are smoke and the gas, sulphur dioxide, from industrial furnaces and domestic fires, and gases in motor vehicle exhausts. The amount of pollution released into the atmosphere has increased enormously during the last fifty years in step with industrial activity.

Normally, when pollutants are discharged into the atmosphere, they are dispersed by the winds and convection currents, and, except near to the source of pollution, they become so dilute as to be virtually harmless. But there are certain atmospheric conditions which prevent rapid dispersion and allow undesirably high concentrations to be reached – hence the importance of meteorology in the question of air pollution. The dilution of pollutant in the air is affected by the wind speed, the gustiness and the atmospheric stability.

It is obvious that the stronger the wind the lower will be the concentration of pollutant in the air. The gustiness is important, particularly on account of the oscillations in wind direction which spreads the pollutants out fanwise instead of restricting them in a narrow thread. For a single source of pollution, such as a power station chimney stack, it is possible to calculate the concentration of pollutant and use such calculations in planning building developments or the location of a power station.

Nowadays large power stations are built with stacks several hundred feet high so that discharged gases rarely become a nuisance. Most air pollution troubles arise from domestic chimneys, which in a large town make up a large collection of many thousands of small sources at low levels. In the London smog of December, 1952, the death rate from respiratory diseases went up to alarming levels. An equally bad smog occurred in London in December, 1962 but without such dire consequences, probably because of regulations which permit the burning of smokeless fuels only.

The name smog is given also to a different type of air pollution which occurs in and around Los Angeles and arises from the action of sunshine on exhaust gases from the very large number of motor vehicles.

Atmospheric instability is conducive to vertical air currents which disperse pollutants to higher levels.

Stability, on the other hand, damps out vertical motion and limits pollutant dispersion.

In calm, cold weather, temperature inversion near the ground causes a high concentration of atmospheric pollution, known as smog; a mixture of smoke and fog.

Weather and industrial activity

Weather affects industrial processes in a variety of ways. For example, the British cotton industry became concentrated in Lancashire partly at least because the humidity was suitable; if the air is too dry the threads are liable to break. This is an example of climate as a factor in the location of an industry. Other examples may be cited in which use is made of the daily forecasts. More ice-cream is consumed on a hot day than a cool one and forecasts, often specially supplied, are helpful to the manufacturers for anticipating the likely demand. Forecasts of dull, wet weather are useful to film companies on location in that they enable timely cancellation of the assembly of equipment and perhaps considerable numbers of people when operation would be impossible. In these examples, reliable forecasts of adverse weather can involve considerable savings for the manufacturer or operator.

High humidity, especially when combined with high temperature, is a cause of the rapid **deterioration of materials** by rusting, rotting or the growth of moulds and fungi. Manufacturers of products destined for overseas, are well advised to take into account the climate in the destination aera and to take the necessary protective measures. In the humid tropics clothing and leather footwear are especially liable to moulds in storage and it is advisable to keep wardrobes warm and dry by the continuous use of a small electric heater. In desert areas exposed objects are subject to abrasion by wind-blown sand. The sand easily penetrates small crevices

so that packaging and storage should be designed to give protection.

In hot dry climates temperatures in thin-walled buildings, railway box wagons and road vans may reach values many degrees higher than the outside air temperature – temperatures of 150°F (65°C) may be reached in corrugated iron sheds in sunshine when the air temperature is about 105°F (40°C). Such temperatures, with a sharp drop at night, are often damaging to some commercial products.

Meteorological services are useful in a number of ways to the **building and construction industries**. Climate data are helpful in design of houses, offices and factories; temperature determines the insulating properties of the walls and the capacity of the heating system; the occurrence of strong and especially gusty winds is a factor in the design of tall buildings and bridges. The famous Tay Bridge disaster of 1879 was caused by exceptionally violent winds. Climatic studies enable estimates to be made of the strongest wind that will occur once in, say 10, 20, 50, 100 . . . years, and these can be taken account of in design. Heavy rain combined with strong winds (driving rain), because of its power of penetrating joints, is another factor to be taken into account in building design. For day to day operations, forecasts of wet weather which prevents outdoor work and impedes traffic on building sites, frost which is damaging to newly-laid concrete, and high winds which make tall cranes hazardous to operate, are the most useful.

Weather lore and weather signs

Over the centuries before the formation of organized meteorological services there have grown up collections of popular sayings about the coming weather based on signs and portents or simply calendar dates. Some of these are merely legendary, some are based on superstition and these have little value except as picturesque sayings. Others derive from the long experience and shrewd observation of shepherds, farmers, sailors and others who follow outdoor occupations. Meteorological studies have shown that these are often soundly based.

An example of purely legendary weather lore is that associated with St. Swithin. The Saint's day occurs on July 15 and legend in England has it that according as the weather on St. Swithin's Day is wet or fine, so it will be for the following forty days. Examination of the weather records over a long period of years has shown that the legend has no foundation.

In the latter part of the last century, a Scottish meteorologist Alexander Buchan examined the temperature records for a number of stations in Scotland and came to the conclusion that there was a tendency for unseasonably cold and warm spells

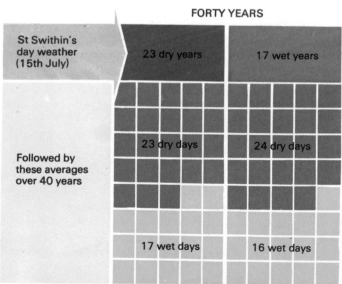

FORTY YEARS

| St Swithin's day weather (15th July) | 23 dry years | 17 wet years |

| Followed by these averages over 40 years | 23 dry days | 24 dry days |
| | 17 wet days | 16 wet days |

Examination of the weather records for St Swithin's day

...ings round the moon' are said to indicate wet weather.

'Red sky at night' is an indication of a clear day to come.

of weather to recur at certain times of the year. Buchan's spells were as follows:–

Cold: Feb 7–14; April 11–14; May 9–14
June 29–July 4; Aug 6–11; Nov. 6–13
Warm: July 12–15; Aug 12–15; Dec 3–14.

These findings attained some notoriety in the press and popular belief too readily extended them to much of Britain. It is now known that they cannot be relied upon as guides to forecasting, though there is a tendency in some years for cold or warm spells to occur at times not too far from the dates listed. In particular, the period somewhere above the second week or middle of May is liable to cold weather in some years; it is especially noticeable because it is liable to cause frost damage to fruit crops after a spell of warm weather. On the continent of Europe these spells are associated with the legendary 'Ice Saints'. A tendency for warm weather to occur about mid-October is associated with St. Luke's Day, October 18. In the United States it is known as 'Indian Summer'.

There is a widespread popular belief that the weather changes with the **Moon** but no evidence has been found to support this belief. In the variable weather of Europe, it is inevitable that many changes of the weather will occur within a day or two on either side of the moon's phases which are separated by only seven days.

Much more reliable than the foregoing are various **signs in the sky** which, coupled with careful observation of the wind and the barometer, enable the amateur to make quite useful forecasts of his local weather. The best of these are the cloud sequences associated with the bad weather of depressions and fronts. An approaching depression and its frontal system show the cloud sequence Cirrus-Cirrostratus-Altostratus-Nimbostratus (pages 52 to 55), white feathery clouds changing to a milky veil followed by a lowering darkening grey pall of cloud; this sequence is a reliable indicator of rain, especially when accompanied by a falling barometer and wind backing from west to south or southeast in the northern hemisphere, west to north or northeast in the southern hemisphere. During the Cirrostratus phase a halo (page 72) frequently appears round the Sun or Moon; the halo is, therefore, justifiably regarded as a sign of imminent rain. The saying:—

'Red sky in the morning is the shepherd's warning,
    Red sky at night is the shepherd's delight.'

is based on the same depression cloud sequence. The morning red sky is caused by the red rays of the rising Sun shining on clouds in the western sky, often Cirrostratus or Altostratus, indicators of rain approaching from the west. The evening red sky means that the western sky is clearing and that the bad weather clouds are passing away to the east.

The early morning sky is sometimes deceptive. In anti-cyclone weather, the day often dawns with a complete cover

The cloud sequence with approaching bad weather

of low grey Stratus which breaks up during the forenoon to be followed by a sunny warm day. On the other hand, especially in the polar air stream behind a depression, cloudless skies in the early morning are often followed by Cumulus and later, Cumulonimbus with showers; hence the saying:–

'Shiny morning, cloudy day,
Cloudy morning, shiny day.'

All these sayings are not, of course, highly reliable; if they were there might be no work for professional forecasters.

Weather control

Weather has to be accepted as it comes. Some provision can be made against it, for example by designing houses and buildings suitable to the climate, or by taking certain precautions such as carrying an umbrella when rain is expected, but there is very little that man can do to control the weather. By and large this is because the amounts of energy involved in weather processes are far too large in relation to man's resources. The energy involved in a single moderate thunderstorm is the equivalent of exploding many hydrogen bombs and it will be recalled that over the whole earth some 1,800 thunderstorms are going on at any one time. Control of weather by brute force seems at present out of the question.

It may be possible, however, by injecting relatively small stimuli into the atmosphere, to trigger off certain natural

processes. This idea has been applied to **rainmaking**.
will be recalled (page 56) that one of the natural rainmaking
processes arises from the simultaneous presence in a cloud
of ice crystals and water drops. In artificial rainmaking,
particles having similar properties to ice crystals (solid carbon
dioxide CO_2 or silver iodide AgI) are introduced into the
cloud to induce the raindrop forming process. Usually the
particles are 'sprayed' from an aircraft flying above the
cloud; this is called Cloud Seeding. Rain has certainly been
brought about in this way – sometimes badly needed rain in
areas affected by drought. Scientific opinion is not yet con-
vinced that the method is a useful one, however, except
possibly over small areas comparable with the size of an
ordinary shower. It is also far from certain that the induced
rain would not have fallen nearby anyway, and that the
operator does not merely cause rain in one place at the expense of another. Any amount of seeding will not, of course,
induce rain if there is not enough moisture in the atmosphere
and suitable clouds have to be selected to have any success.

Another method of seeding is to use a long line of
generators which release silver iodide. The particles are
carried up into the cloud by atmospheric turbulence and
convection. The method has been applied in Britain to warm
front situations, the object being to induce rainfall over the
drier parts of eastern England a hundred miles or so down-

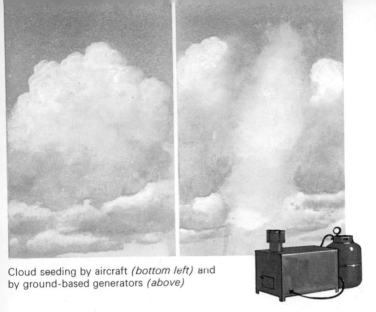

Cloud seeding by aircraft *(bottom left)* and
by ground-based generators *(above)*

stream from the generators. There was no real evidence that
rainfall was usefully increased by this method.

An example of the 'brute force' method was the **dispersal
of fog** on military airfields during the Second World War.
Oil burners spaced along the runway generated enough heat to
disperse fog long enough for individual aircraft to land. This
method is far too expensive for commercial use.

There are at present a very few suggested methods of
altering the climate which come just within the realm of
the possible. One is to dam the Bering Strait between Siberia
and Alaska, stopping the cold current from the Arctic which
flows down the coast of northeast Siberia and is partly
responsible for the inhospitable climate there. It is not known,
however, how this would affect the inflow of warmer water
to the Arctic by way of the northeast Atlantic. Another is to
melt the Arctic Ocean ice by nuclear power. Though these
might improve the climate of some regions, there is no
certainty that climate would not be worsened in others. In
fact, before any climatic modification is attempted, the world
wide effects should be assessed. This could only be done by
using much more powerful computers than exist at the
present time.

BOOKS TO READ

The books listed below are suitable for the general reader; advanced textbooks are not included.

A Course in Elementary Meteorology by the Meteorological Office. HMSO, 1962.

Climate in Everyday Life by C. E. P. Brooks. English University Press, London, 1950.

Climate Through the Ages by C. E. P. Brooks. Ernest Benn, London, 1949.

Climatology by A. Austin Miller. Methuen & Co., London, 1961.

Climatology by W. G. Kendrew. Clarendon Press, Oxford, 1957.

Cloud Study, a Pictorial Guide by F. H. Ludlam and R. S. Scorer. John Murray, London, 1957.

Elementary Meteorology by G. F. Taylor. Prentice Hall Inc., New York, 1954.

Everday Meteorology by A. Austin Miller and M. Parry. Hutchinson, London, 1958.

Introduction to Meteorology by S. Petterssen. McGraw-Hill, London and New York, 1941.

Meteorology for Mariners by the Meteorological Office. HMSO, 1967.

Our American Weather by G. H. T. Kimble. McGraw-Hill, New York, 1955.

Radar Observes the Weather by L. J. Battan. Heineman Educational Books London, 1962.

The Climates of the Continents by W. G. Kendrew. Clarendon Press, Oxford, 1957.

The Meteorological Glossary by the Meteorological Office. HMSO, 1963.

The Ways of the Weather by J. S. Sawyer. Adam and Charles Black, London, 1957.

The Weather Map by the Meteorological Office. HMSO, 1956.

Understanding Weather by O. G. Sutton. Penguin Books, 1964.

Weather. A periodical published monthly by the Royal Meteorological Society, London.

Weather and Agriculture by J. A. Taylor. Pergamon, London, 1967.

Weather and Man by H. H. Neuberger and F. B. Stephens. Prentice Hall Inc., New York, 1948.

Weather Lore by R. Inwards revised by E. L. Hawke. Rider & Co., London, 1950.

Weatherwise. A periodical published bi-monthly by the American Meteorological Society, Boston.

Weatherwise Gardening by L. P. Smith and S. A. Searle. Blandford Press, London, 1958.

SOME OTHER TITLES IN THIS SERIES

Natural History

The Animal Kingdom
Australian Animals
Bird Behaviour
Birds of Prey
Fishes of the World
Fossil Man
A Guide to the Seashore

Life in the Sea
Mammals of the World
Natural History Collecting
The Plant Kingdom
Prehistoric Animals
Snakes of the World
Wild Cats

Gardening

Chrysanthemums
Garden Flowers

Garden Shrubs
Roses

Popular Science

Atomic Energy
Computers at Work
Electronics

Mathematics
Microscopes & Microscopic Life

Arts

Architecture
Jewellery

Porcelain
Victoriana

General Information

Flags
Military Uniforms
Rockets & Missiles
Sailing

Sailing Ships & Sailing Craft
Sea Fishing
Trains

Domestic Animals and Pets

Budgerigars
Cats
Dogs

Horses & Ponies
Pets for Children

Domestic Science

Flower Arranging

History & Mythology

Discovery of
  Africa
  North America
  The American West
  Japan

Myths & Legends of
  Ancient Egypt
  Ancient Greece
  The South Seas